The Hackensack Water Company
1869-1969

The Hackensack Water Company

1869-1969

ADRIAN C. LEIBY

in collaboration with

Nancy Wichman

B | C
H | S

Bergen County Historical Society

River Edge, New Jersey

1969

Acknowledgements

The story of the trials and tribulations of the men and women who made it their job to preserve the water supply of the Hackensack Valley and to deliver it to the people of the Valley is but a small footnote to the history of northern Hudson County and Bergen County in New Jersey, and Rockland County, New York, but I have gotten a great deal of pleasure from learning something of the last hundred years in this part of the country and hope that I have been able to pass some of it on.

I was more than fortunate to have Miss Nancy Wichman as a researcher on the project. Nancy, who was then a graduate student in American History at the University of Michigan, collected enough material about the period from 1869 to 1919 to write half a dozen books about the Hackensack Valley and set before me a task far beyond my abilities to use it properly. I also have on my conscience the matter of persuading her to give up the study of history and to study law. She is now practising in New York City. Delighted as I am to have her in the legal profession, I hope that her scholarly mind will not be wholly lost to history and that she will never cease to carry on her historical work as an avocation.

I am indebted to Mr. Fred Bogert and Mr. James Ransom for reviewing the text. Mr. George H. Buck, Mr. Samuel W. Zerman, and Miss Helen Kremen have made many helpful suggestions. Mr. Emile J. Fricker, whose connection with the

Company has spanned nearly two-thirds of its one hundred year history, Mr. Julius Von Scheidt, and others, have supplied many anecdotes about early Company affairs. I must confess that in the case of several such anecdotes, taken from the common fund of Company lore and doubtless much altered in everyone's telling, I have used the version that I am familiar with, and not their suggested alternatives. Anyone who believes that the particular version in the book is wrong should direct his criticism at me and not at them, for they may well agree with the criticism.

Mr. Howard Durie, an authority on the history of northern Bergen County, gave me many facts about Woodcliff. Mr. Edwin D. Veldran furnished information about his father's mill, and the late Miss Helen Waite did the same for the Van Buskirk Mill owned by her grandfather at the site of the New Milford Pumping Station. I was more than fortunate to have the help of Mr. Melvin E. King, who was the Timekeeper on the 1911 Oradell Reservoir project and to discover that, besides much old Oradell lore, he had many photographs taken by his father in the days before the 1902 reservoir was built.

The Bergenfield, Oradell, Englewood and Teaneck libraries have been most helpful, as was the Stevens Institute of Technology Library and others. The newspaper archives of the Johnson Free Public Library have been invaluable, and its staff very helpful.

It would be wrong to write these paragraphs without mentioning another debt. Bergen County historians have been blessed far beyond their deserts by the county's newspapers for the past century. The *Bergen County Journal, Bergen County Democrat,* the *Bergen Index,* the *Hackensack Republican,* the *Englewood Times,* the *Englewood Press* and the *Bergen Evening Record* (now the *Record*), among others, have all been great newspapers, edited by men with a flair for the newsworthy stories that provide the flesh to cover the bare bones of history. The *Hudson Dispatch,* in Hudson County, and the *Journal-News* of Rockland County deserve the same praise. Mr. Eben Winton of the *Democrat,* one of the incorporators of the Water Company, Mr. Cornelius Christie of the *Index,* the writer and scholar, the peppery Eugene K. Bird of the *Republican* and several capable editors of the *Record,* to speak of but a few, have been great newspapermen, many of whose writings bear up as well today as they did when they were first written decades ago. This book could not have been written without them.

The help that I was given in finding the illustrations deserves a special word. Mr. Norman Nielson pulled out several packing cases of Company pictures and spent hours reviewing them with Mrs. Leiby and me. Mr. Fred Van Dyke, besides being responsible for most of the modern pictures, copied dozens of borrowed pictures with his usual great skill. Mr. Don E. Carter, Executive Editor of the *Record,* located a number of early pictures, of which Mr. Gerry de la Ree's postcard collection was particularly helpful. Mr. Howard Durie and Mr. and Mrs. John Fischer went to considerable trouble to get pictures of early Woodcliff; Mr. and Mrs. Fred W. Bogert found family pictures of the country near the Cherry Hill Reservoir, which stood on the farm where Mrs. Bogert was born, and her brother, Mr. Harold B. Zabriskie, a distinguished engineer, went to great trouble to collect enough evidence to reconstruct a plan of the original Cherry Hill Reservoir. Mr. J. Tucker Ames, who worked for the White Motor Company as a young college graduate, furnished the picture of the 1905 White Steamer. Mr. John Zehner, of the Tappan Zee Historical Society, went out of his way to help also.

Mrs. Evelyn Shaw Anderson has typed and retyped drafts and redrafts, on and off hours, so often that I am almost embarrassed to bring the subject back to mind by expressing my thanks.

I was told many years ago that it is wrong to thank your editor, because it is an editor's job to correct writer's mistakes. In my case, first, it is not Emorie Leiby's business to edit; second, she has more than enough other historical work to do; and, third, an editor who receives no better copy than she, deserves thanks even if it were her job to edit. I am deeply grateful for her help. It may be equally unprofessional to thank the man responsible for manufacturing a book, but I cannot close without a word of thanks to Mr. Robert W. Perkins, an old pro in every good sense of the term, a man with a deep knowledge of printing and design that only forty years of experience can supply.

A. C. L.

Contents

Illustrations

The Hackensack Water Company
1869-1969

Schooners Tied Up at Anderson Lumber Yard Dock, Hackensack, c. 1869
Unknown Artist; Collection of Bergen County Historical Society

1869

The tides in the affairs of men do not fit neatly into the system of numbers that mortals assign to passing years, and it is of course nothing more than happenstance that the three particular decades, 1669-1679, 1769-1779 and 1869-1879, exactly a century apart, have marked such profound changes in the Hackensack Valley. There can be no doubt, however, that they did. Before 1669 there were no permanent settlements in the Valley; in the ten years between 1669 and 1679 nearly all of its land was patented and it began to fill up with the Dutch, French and English families who made up almost its entire population for the next two hundred years. Between 1769 and 1779, the Hackensack Valley went through its most traumatic experience in three hundred years, in fact one of the most traumatic experiences that any part of America has ever suffered, when it lay as a neutral ground between the British and American armies during the Revolution and brother fought brother for seven years of bitter civil war. The effects of that conflict lasted for a great part of the next century and a half. Between 1869 and 1879, the Valley stepped from the age of husbandry into the age of industry and finance, the age in which, for better or worse, we all live today.

Before the 1860's Bergen County was a community of thriving, contented, Jersey Dutch farmers, by no means unaware of the great world around them or the great city that consumed their produce and made them rich, but content to live in their own plain Jersey Dutch ways, with their barns full to the bursting point and their cattle fat, striving like their ancestors always to be neat and cleanly, and never to complain of an empty purse.

By 1869, however, Bergen County could no longer stand aloof from New York City and a nation which, in the years immediately following the Civil War, as one historian has said,

> "had had a great vision, had surrendered to its imagination. Eager, bold, expansive minds, many of them constructive geniuses of the highest ability, had come to the fore during and after the War and were being carried to a commanding national and international position."

Bergen County had also surrendered to the new vision. A visitor to Hackensack, the county seat, would have been blind indeed not to have seen that it was a shining example of a self-respecting, self-confident and self-disciplined American community of the day, filled with enterprising men who were directing their considerable talents to making themselves and their nation prosperous. The sound of hammers and saws was heard everywhere, the stores were crowded with people and the tree-lined streets filled with carriages and wagons. The town had always been a pleasant place; it was now attaining a certain elegance.

> "The streets [, one visitor wrote, are] lined with attractive dwellings of the well-to-do business men of the metropolis. Upon every hand the skill of the architect is noticeable, challenging comparison with each other in efforts to construct handsome villas. . . . Hackensack's situation is one of the most delightful in the whole country, the river affording communication with the outside world, as well as adding to the attractiveness of the place during the summer months." (*The Industries of New Jersey, Part 6* [*New York 1883*], *page 1009.*)

2

The population, which had been no more than one thousand twenty years before, was fast approaching four thousand, and promised to go much higher. Most of the people in town bore Jersey Dutch names: Voorhis, Van Buskirk, Banta, Wortendyke, Huyler, Ackerson, Demarest, Ackerman, Anderson, Berry, Vanderbeek, Terhune, Jacobson, Auryanson, Bogart, Blanch, Christie, Westervelt, Berdan, Doremus, Vreeland, Lydecker, Brinckerhoff and Blauvelt, but more and more Englishmen and Germans had been settling there recently: the Gamewells, the Fairs, the Poors, the Atwells, the Zingsems, and the Haas', for example, most of them well-to-do business men of the metropolis, whose presence added to the new spirit and bustle in the old town. More recently many of other backgrounds had joined them. There were now four or five hundred Roman Catholics in town, and in 1866 they built a fine new church on Maple Street in the northern part of the village.

The editor of the *Bergen County Democrat* put it very well in November, 1868:

> "Hackensack appears to be imbued with the spirit of improvement which seems to know no cessation. There are now perhaps forty new buildings being erected. Our village has doubled its population within a few years and yet they come. We have all the comforts and appliances of city life, with the advantage of cheaper living. Our sidewalks have been greatly improved, our streets are lighted with gas, and our omnibus line to and from the Rail Road Depot is a great accommodation, while our "New Depot" vies in convenience and comfort with any village in the state. Jersey being the only outlet for the superabundant population of the City, the attraction of our village will induce hundreds of others, wealthy and discriminating citizens, to settle in our midst, and thus enjoy our advantages and contiguity to the city." *(Bergen County Democrat, Nov. 13, 1868)*

First Reformed Church, Hackensack, c. 1859
Bergen County Historical Society

(Looking back at Hackensack a half century later, Eugene K. Bird, the editor of the *Hackensack Republican*, who had come to town at about that time, remembered that the street lights were "the faintest imaginable gas jets, [where] mortals, immersed in more than ordinary impenetrable gloom, stumbled along on crosslaid board walks that resented the pressure of feet by flying up endwise and punishing the poor wight." The streets probably looked bright enough to Mr. Bird when he first saw them.)

The Hackensack & New York Railroad was busy constructing an extension to Hillsdale and planning to extend further north to the Hudson River at Haverstraw. Subscriptions were already being taken up for railroad stations at Central Avenue and Anderson Street, and builders were busy erecting the homes that would be needed as soon as the new stations were in use. If proof were needed of the prospects of Hackensack, the news in March, 1869, that the railroad barons of the Erie had purchased the Hackensack & New York provided it. They knew a good thing when they saw it.

A group of local men had subscribed $75,000 for a project considerably more daring than the short Hackensack & New York Railroad, a project to bring a railroad from Jersey City through Hackensack, north and west into New York State and ultimately to the Great Lakes at Oswego, a line to be called, locally, the New Jersey Midland Railroad. The Hackensack & New York Railroad, which came up from its junction with the Erie along the western edge of the Hackensack meadows, had its station a half mile west of Main Street; the New Jersey Mid-

First Locomotive on Hackensack & New York Railroad
Walter A. Lucas Collection

land Railroad would have a large passenger station in the very center of town, on the site of the old County Clerk's Office. With a second railroad projected and building, the town could hardly fail to grow even faster.

Main Street itself reflected all the new population and prosperity. Lined with trees, it began at a willow-shaded park, surrounded by "a neat fence consisting of stout bars of iron running through substantial wooden posts painted brown", which had once been called the church "plain" (after the Dutch "pleyn", or square), but was now coming to be known by the more elegant English term, "the Green." Around the Green stood a number of impressive buildings: the Bergen County Court House, built in 1819, the third on the site, a two-story building in the style of the Federal period; next to that, the large and commodious Hackensack House, a new three-story hotel; across the Green, the Mansion House where George Washington and his staff were quartered in November, 1776, when it was the stately new home of Judge Peter Zabriskie; and to the east, the eighteenth-century First Reformed Church. The church was about to be reopened and rededicated after extensive reconstruction, further evidence of the prosperous times. (The rival True Reformed Church had been considerably enlarged two years earlier.) To the east, along the river, schooners brought lumber from the south to lumberyards that were busy supplying materials for the new buildings. On the west side of the Green, across Main Street, stood another ancient landmark, Campbell's Tavern, where Archibald Campbell had served General Washington's meals when he was at the Zabriskie mansion. The tavern was now somewhat shabby and run down after seventy-five years as a grog-shop, post office, general store and meeting place for the idle and shiftless men of town who had enough money in their pockets to buy a mug or two of beer and enough interest in county politics to lounge around near the Court House.

It had probably changed little from the time, in the winter of 1831, when an unfriendly visitor reported that

> "In the center [of its large bar room] stood an old-fashioned ten-plate stove, surrounded by fifteen or twenty large lazy

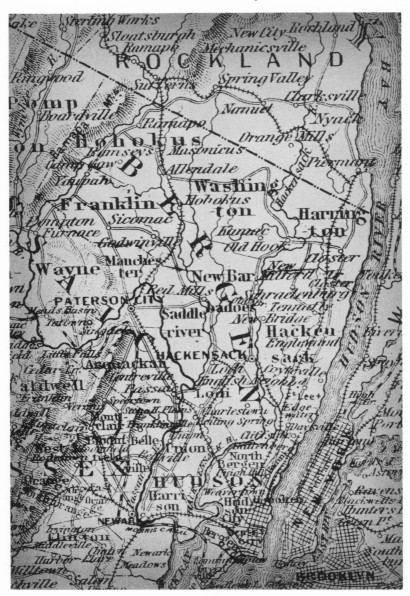

Map of Bergen, Hudson and Rockland Counties, 1869
A. J. Johnson, New York

looking fellows. On the stove (which was very hot) stood
a number of pots, mugs, pitchers and jars of beer, brandy,
ale and cider; some, running over with the heat, made a
hissing and a noise, and the fumes which rose to the ceiling, . . . intermixed with clouds of pipe and cigar smoke,
. . . nearly shut out the light of day . . ." (*Grant Thorburn,
Forty Years Residence in America*, p. 143.)

South of the Court House, at the bridge which carried the
Bergen Turnpike over Hackensack Creek, the sail boats of the
river fishermen were tied up to tempt the ladies of the town
with their catches.

Like many towns in the center of a prosperous farming area,
Hackensack was much more of a commercial center than might
have been expected in a town of four thousand people. Near the
Green one store stood next to another along Main Street, and
stores were interspersed with residences as far as Anderson
Street, a mile to the north. At the second door above the Mansion
House, N. Vreeland & Son had just opened a stove and furnace
establishment, from which they also carried on a business as
plumbers and roofers. On the corner of Main and Bridge Streets
was R. P. Terhune's Hardware Emporium, which was prospering greatly in the building boom. Mr. Terhune, who lived in a
large, elegant house in Lodi Township, was one of the founders
of the Hackensack Gas Company and a promoter and director of
the New Jersey Midland Railroad. Near by, John W. Terhune's
"Oyster, Confectionary and Ice Cream Saloon" attracted many
to its cool interior. On the corner of Bergen Street stood the
apothecary of M. W. Heath. Mr. Heath boasted a good stock
of drugs, and, he advertised, "unites with his pharmaceutical efforts the position of dentist as well, [being] recognized as . . .
particularly skillful in drawing teeth and making plates for the
mouth, so that the natural expression is retained." He was also
engaged in the stationery business. A little further along Mr. W.

Furby (who, a business directory wrote, had "a sympathetic and agreeable manner, which are deemed indispensable to one in that line of business") maintained an undertaking establishment. Mrs. Furby operated a fancy goods store a few doors away.

Beyond that was the modest store-front office and press of Eben Winton's *Bergen County Democrat*. One had only to read the pages of advertising in the *Democrat* to see what a busy place Hackensack was; few goods were being sold in New York which were not being offered at local stores.

At Warren Street stood the Washington Institute, built in 1841 on the site of the celebrated Peter Wilson's Academy, one of America's foremost educational centers when it was founded in 1769. For the last four years the building had housed a public school free of tuition, and more recently free of any charge whatever, even for books and paper. One hundred fifty students were enrolled and a hundred more were seeking admission from other towns and villages in the County. North of the Institute there were seven or eight houses on the west side of the street before one reached the carefully tended grounds of the new home of Charles H. Voorhis, one of Hackensack's most prominent young lawyers, a man who was to have a large part in the beginnings of the Hackensack Water Company. The Voorhis house was a very model of modern architecture, with ceiling-high windows rounded at the top in the front parlor, and heavy cornices braced with carefully designed woodwork. The high front porch was decorated with charming frescoes, two large hemlocks guarded the walk to the door, and the fence surrounding the property was a carpenter's masterpiece. Hitching posts awaited arriving guests, and the new trees that grew at the edge of the flagstone sidewalk were protected from the teeth of the guests' horses with tastefully designed wooden standards. Behind the house stood a carriage house and a sizeable barn.

North of the Voorhis place, Main Street went on for several

Residence of Charles H. Voorhis, Main Street, Hackensack
1876 Bergen County Atlas

miles, with new houses and businesses everywhere. Next to Mr. Voorhis' house stood the residence of W. H. Berry and his thirty-year-old Carriage Repository, busy making, as it advertised, Carriages, Coaches, Top and No-Top Buggies, Market, Grocery and Express Wagons, Phaetons, Dog Carts, Rockaways, Coupes and Cabriolets. A few hundred feet beyond, Wortendyke & Demarest's huge store stood in the middle of a three or four-acre landscaped tract. Further along the west side, far back from the street, on a four-acre plot, was the large house of William S. Banta, a local lawyer of even more prominence than Charles H. Voorhis. The house could hardly be recognized as the old Banta farmhouse behind its new frescoed porches and the fretwork decorating its roof, all surrounded by large trees. Banta, one of the most progressive men in town, had benefited largely from being a Republican in a heavily Democratic county during the late Civil War, more respected and better known for his energy and enterprise than warmly regarded by the old Bergen County Democratic establishment. The *Democrat* had regularly verged on libel in reporting his activities during the War, when he held a number of local offices under Federal patronage. The leading attorney of Hackensack, he was involved in many local enterprises and was now busily helping the promoters of the Ridgefield Park Railroad to establish a line to the north along the east bank of the Hackensack which, on a somewhat different route, later became the West Shore branch of the New York Central. He, too, was to have a part in the early history of the Hackensack Water Company.

Further to the north, more new houses bordered the treelined sidewalks, some of them even more impressive than the Voorhis and Banta places. G. N. Zingsem was, in point of fact, building a whole new town of Victorian villas, in a development which he called Fairmount. He had just sold a half interest in a large tract of land to the Hackensack Extension Railroad for $100,000, and he lived in a palatial wooden mansion surrounded by acres of landscaped grounds in the center of his development. Nor was Hackensack any longer a one-street town. Essex Street boasted many beautiful estates like the residence of John Huyler, former Judge of the State Court of Errors and Appeals, Speaker of the State Assembly and a leading proslavery figure in Congress in the years before the War. Even more magnificent were the Gamewell home on State Street (owned by the head of the American Fire Alarm Telegraph Company), and the estate on Terrace Street (Polifly Road), west of the railroad station, owned by E. E. Poor, the President of the National Park Bank, one of New York's most important financial institutions.

In short, in the last few years, Hackensack had changed from a complacent country village filled with well-to-do merchants, lawyers and retired farmers, descendants of the people who settled the Hackensack Valley two centuries before, into a cosmopolitan suburban town, where the old County families found themselves rubbing shoulders with dozens of enterprising and successful New York bankers and business men, men with wide-ranging interests who thought in millions of dollars, not in the thousands that had once seemed large to local people. Everywhere mansard-roofed mansions rose next to gambrel-roofed Dutch sandstone houses, and here and there carpenters were busy tearing off ancient gambrel roofs to substitute new mansard roofs and removing plain Dutch stoops to add modern frescoed porches.

*　　*　　*

It was obvious that burgeoning Hackensack could not long continue to rely on back-yard wells and cisterns for a water supply and the subject of a public water system was much in the minds of its residents; in fact two important local people were already taking steps to promote such a system. Charles H. Voorhis, probably acting for his client, G. N. Zingsem, had obtained a charter for a Cherry Hill Water and Gas Company two years earlier but had done nothing as yet to put the charter into use, and in recent months Garret Ackerson, the leader of the dominant Democratic Party in the County, had been seeking a water charter with somewhat more extensive powers than the Cherry Hill charter. He proposed to form a Hackensack Water Company to serve the village and the surrounding country and for that purpose to use any of the nearby streams. In those days charters were granted by special Acts of the Legislature. The Hackensack Water Company bill passed the Senate without opposition on February 24, 1869, and on March 12, 1869, Governor Randolph signed it into law.

Voorhis and Ackerson, besides being determined political antagonists, represented two wholly different kinds of Jersey Dutchman, both highly successful, the one with state-wide, even nation-wide, interests; the other, like his ancestors, rooted in Bergen County and interested in little that did not affect his neighbors and himself.

Charles H. Voorhis, perhaps more than anyone else in town, was a man of the new age, unfettered by the old-fashioned conservative business practices, the Democratic politics and the Calvinist puritanism of the Jersey Dutch who had controlled the County for a century. He was born in Spring Valley (Paramus),

Birthplace of Charles H. Voorhis,
Spring Valley (Paramus), New Jersey,
1876 Bergen County Atlas

Bergen County, a few miles north of Hackensack, on March 13, 1833, in a house in which five generations of Voorhis' had lived. He went to a nearby log school under the tutelage of the Honorable Jacob R. Wortendyke, a man of high intellectual calibre who later became a famous lawyer and a member of Congress. Voorhis graduated from Rutgers College in 1853 as valedictorian of his class, moved to Jersey City, where he taught in a classical academy and studied law under the distinguished Chancellor Abraham O. Zabriskie, and was admitted to the bar in 1856. He then opened a law office in Jersey City, to which he commuted the rest of his life. With his excellent Bergen County connections, he was named counsel for the Northern Railroad as soon as that line was completed in the late fifties, and he moved to Teaneck when passenger service to Jersey City began. In 1860 he moved from Teaneck to Hackensack, and built his home next to the Earle family homestead, the old farmhouse on Main Street in which his wife had been born.

His father, Henry H. Voorhis, was one of the most respected men in Bergen County, a pillar of Jersey Dutch virtue, one of the leading figures in that most Jersey Dutch of institutions, the True Reformed Dutch Church, and the founder and head of the Bergen County Mutual Fire Insurance Company. His mother was a great grand-daughter of the celebrated Dutch divine, John Henry Goetschius, the founder of Rutgers College, his Alma Mater. He himself was able to speak Jersey Dutch (so far as colloquialisms were concerned, the *Democrat* said grudgingly), a valuable asset in a county where that was the vernacular of many voters. Charles Voorhis had little patience with the old ways, and quickly made it evident that he saw no reason not to be as modern as the next man merely because he was a Jersey Dutchman.

He supported the incumbent Democratic President, James Buchanan, before the War, and was one of the most active supporters of Stephen A. Douglas in the 1860 election. When the War started, he defied the general opinion of the County by taking a strong stand against slavery, and by deserting the party of his ancestors—who without exception had been Revolutionary War Whigs and Jeffersonian Democrats—to join a state-wide coalition of Republicans, Douglas Democrats and members of the one-time Constitutional Union Party to form a Union Party in New Jersey, which nominated Marcus L. Ward of Newark for Governor in 1862. (Abraham Lincoln himself was reelected in 1864 not as a Republican but as the candidate of the national Union Party.) Before long, Voorhis and most other Union Party members became full-fledged members of the Republican Party.

Charles H. Voorhis
Library of Congress

In 1864, he was a delegate to the national convention that re-nominated Lincoln; he was said to be a personal friend of both Lincoln and General Grant, who had few enough supporters in Bergen County or elsewhere in New Jersey. His next move was equally defiant, and, many thought, not unrelated to his politics.

Shortly after the outset of the War, six local people, principally New Yorkers who had recently moved to Hackensack, organized an Episcopal Church. Though the new church was plain evidence that the village was changing from a sleepy Dutch county seat to a cosmopolitan city, we may be sure that there were some Hackensack people who were not overpleased, particularly when it became known that Charles Voorhis (and soon after, several other well-connected young men of Dutch background) joined in the move. Within a short time he became one of the most prominent Episcopalian laymen in the State, a member of the Standing Committee of the Diocese of Northern New Jersey, a Trustee of the Episcopal Theological Seminary in New York, a Trustee of Burlington College, and a founder and one of the trustees of the flourishing new Hackensack Academy, an Episcopalian-oriented school which was busy preparing young men of the town for college. Voorhis' defection from the church of his fathers was particularly distressing to many because he was the son of an elder of the famous Schraalenburgh True Reformed Dutch Church, a father who prided himself on being plain Dutch, indifferent to social position and far removed from the effete ways of the great City, and known throughout the County as the very embodiment of the simple virtues of hard work, thrift and hatred of ostentation.

If leaving the church of his fathers had not been enough to set him at variance with the Dutch patriarchy, he also began while yet in his early thirties to take a leading position in every new business enterprise in town, showing little deference to his elders. Moreover, while they themselves delved and span for their modest competences, Charles Voorhis appeared to have amassed a great fortune with no regard whatever for the Biblical injunction, so highly esteemed by the Dutch, that thou shalt eat bread only in the sweat of thy face.

Voorhis had been one of the first to anticipate the land boom that had burst upon Bergen County, acquiring large amounts of acreage and many town lots in Hackensack and elsewhere. An eighty-four acre tract he had bought years ago when it was an outlying farm now stood next to the new Central Avenue railroad station, property which itself would have been fortune enough for most people. Some of the established people of the town thought Voorhis pushful, and many of them did not hesitate to say that most of his huge landholdings were mortgaged to the hilt—a particularly grievous offense to Jersey Dutchmen, who preferred to live simply and to hold rather than sign mortgages —but no one could deny that he was eminently successful. People were beginning to say openly that he was Bergen County's first millionaire. As the *Democrat* put it,

> "It is not easy to determine the precise wealth of Mr. Voorhis, and, as he is extremely reticent on this point, no more can be said here than that he is likely, in a few years, to be numbered among our American millionaires. He is one of the largest landholders in Bergen County, and believes firmly in real estate. . . .
>
> "He helped the Midland Railroad to come through Hackensack by subscribing to $5,000 worth of its stock, and deeding to it seven acres of land besides, and he is one of the bondholders' committee of the New Jersey & New York Railroad. In short he is interested in every project of improvement hereabouts. . . . The result of his labors will be better appreciated perhaps ten years hence than they can be now, and hundreds will revere his memory long after he has departed." *(Bergen County Democrat, June 15, 1877.)*

Voorhis was also one of the small group of Republicans credited with wresting control of the State government from the Democrats by electing Marcus Ward as Republican Governor in 1865, and a Republican Assembly and Senate in 1866 and 1867. It was said that Voorhis was personally responsible for inducing Ward, a prominent Newark business man, to run for the office. He himself was named Judge of Common Pleas in 1868, the chief county office. Though the Democrats had elected a governor in 1868 and taken possession of both houses of the legislature in 1868 and 1869 so that the local Republicans no longer controlled State patronage, by the beginning of 1869 the national political situation had greatly strengthened the hand of Voorhis and his Republican friends.

General Grant had been inaugurated on March 4, 1869, with general acclaim, and the whole country hoped that the strong, silent man who took the oath that morning would bring a new era of purpose and prosperity to the nation. Voorhis was reputed to be close to General Grant, and it took little political sophistication to see that control of local Federal appointments might be decisive in local elections.

Voorhis was one of the first to see the need for local public improvements. Shortly after the Hackensack Improvement Commission was founded in 1868 and took over the municipal government of Hackensack, Voorhis and Robert W. Goslee, incensed at the do-nothing attitude of its first members, sought and obtained places on the Commission and proceeded with two other like-minded members under Voorhis' leadership first to deadlock the eight-man Commission and then to reform it. An era of intense local excitement and bad feeling followed. Even his opponents, however, later conceded that

> "The issue . . . was a good deal in Judge Voorhis' favor, besides giving the village well graded streets, pavements for the sidewalks . . . and other much needed improvements— a condition no progressive man would wish to see abolished now, whatever difference of opinion there may be about the prematureness of the work." *(Bergen County Democrat, June 15, 1877.)*

Voorhis' faction lost the County election in 1869. The *Bergen County Democrat* headlined its story on November 5, 1869: "Charley Voorhis and His Corporal's Guard Driven in Their Holes", but everyone knew that whether they won or lost Voorhis and his allies had broken the hold of the old Democratic regime on the County and were making a strong bid at every election to put their men into every county and state office.

Bergen County Court House, 1876
1876 Bergen County Atlas

Garret Ackerson, Jr., the other holder of a water company charter, was in many ways the antithesis of Charles H. Voorhis. Though both were sons of farmer-businessmen of good families, Ackerson had little formal education (few leading citizens of the County of his day did), and had amassed his small fortune in modest amounts over many years. He had built up public confidence and respect over an equally long time and, like most Jersey Dutchmen, prided himself, not on his quick wits, but on his standing in the community. As the undisputed leader of the dominant Democratic party in the County, no one doubted that he knew the uses of power. His enemies put it more sharply, complaining that he sat "like a king on his throne in the village of Hackensack . . . making bargains years ahead."

He lived in a large house surrounded by extensive landscaped grounds, just south of the Court House across Hackensack

Creek on Hudson Street, and was perhaps the most widely respected man in the County. Fifty-three years old and at the height of his career in 1869, Judge Ackerson (the title came from his county office, not from any judicial background) had been born in Pascack, the son of a prosperous farmer who had been a major general in the New Jersey militia in the War of 1812. Garret was educated in the Pascack district schools and had himself been an officer of the militia since he was fifteen years old. The *Hackensack Republican* wrote at the time of his death that he had

> "received his early political training in a school calculated to develop the natural tact, soundness of judgment and capacity in leadership which enabled him subsequently to attain and hold, for so long a period, the control of his party in Bergen County."

There could be little doubt of the truth of this observation. In 1839, at the age of 23, he was elected assessor of old Harrington township, which then included Pascack, in a campaign which Judge Ackerson himself later described as one full of excitement and fire, besides which the boisterous canvasses of the 1860's were as Quaker meetings.

> "The most memorable election of that period was on the division of the township, Pascack wishing to separate from the eastern part, which made a strong fight in opposition. The voters 'passed through the gate', making the process tedious and giving unusual opportunity for discussion and collision between factions. When the voting was held at Pascack, the Closterites descended upon the polling place in force and a desperate fight ensued, in which Jacob Van Buskirk, of New Milford, had a narrow escape from being beaten to death. . . .

> "In 1845, when 29 years of age, Judge Ackerson was elected

County Clerk, the first Democrat to attain that distinction. . . . From this time forward the leadership of the party practically rested upon 'Garry' Ackerson, and he was not only a leader in name, but in fact.

"From 1845 to 1880 there was little work of a public nature in Hackensack with which Judge Ackerson was not directly or indirectly identified. When he reached the town to assume the duties of County Clerk there was a population of about 1,000. The County Clerk's office was a little one-story building facing the west side of Main Street on the site of the Susquehanna railroad crossing. There was then no Union or Park Streets, and no houses on State Street north of the present railroad; west of State Street was a stretch of excellent farm land to the hill; there was no house on the east side of Main Street for several blocks in the center of town."

He became the counselor and banker of many of the County's Dutch farmers, who, in the days when there were no trustworthy banks, used the county vaults to hold their gold and silver awaiting investment. In 1855, after Colonel Ackerson had served as County Clerk and leader of the Democratic party in the County for ten years, his name was put in nomination for a third term. Opponents, annoyed at Ackerson's one-man rule, nominated the young lawyer, W. S. Banta, who was aided by the open defection from the Democratic party of George Doremus, Henry H. Voorhis and his son, Charles H. Voorhis, and many Democrats in the northwest part of the County.

The election, it is said, "resulted in one of the few really great political contests in Bergen County." Ackerson was elected by the narrow margin of 149. His supremacy in the County was not challenged again for twenty years, but he won the election at the cost of a permanent division of the party. When the Civil War came, the regular Democrats opposed it, and the Democrats who had revolted against Ackerson five years before became the leading supporters of the Union cause, either (as in the case of Henry H. Voorhis) as War Democrats or (as in the case of W. S. Banta and Charles Voorhis) as open Republicans. When Banta and Voorhis were particularly eloquent in denouncing the evils of slavery during the War, some sceptical Jersey Dutchmen of the County doubtless recalled the bitterness of the earlier election and wondered whether slavery might not have worn a different aspect to the speakers if they, and not Garry Ackerson, had won control of the Democratic party in the 1855 contest.*

In the 1850's Judge Ackerson had become the head of Hackensack's militia and had been commissioned its lieutenant-colonel. In 1869, most people in town still remembered the Fourth of July annual training days before the Civil War, when the local "train band", called the Continentals, would meet on the Green in their drab knee breeches and vests, blue coats and tricorn hats, and go through what passed for military maneuvers before the eyes of the local citizens. Everyone over eighteen years of age was required to train for ten years, and it was the one day in the year when everyone in town got together for a holiday. Garret Ackerson wore white trousers and a blue coat, a tall officer's hat with a long red plume in front, and a red sash under his blue coat, a uniform more reminiscent of soldiers of the Mexican War than the Continental Line. Spirits and food were

---

* Actually, the independent course which Voorhis and W. S. Banta followed probably traced to their clerkships in the office of Chancellor Abraham O. Zabriskie. Zabriskie had been a leading lawyer in Hackensack in the 1840's, serving as County Prosecutor for a time and later as Surrogate, and subsequently moving his offices to Jersey City, where he was named Chancellor of the State, one of its two principal judges. He was one of the old-line leaders of New Jersey's Whig party who left it in 1856 to form a new party (then called the "Opposition" party, since the name Republican was identified with the then unpopular Abolitionist movement). He had since become conspicuous for his opposition to slavery and his support for protective tariffs, and may well have influenced his two proteges.

Garret Ackerson, Jr.
Bergen County Democrat History of Hackensack;
Johnson Free Public Library

on sale around the Green and bystanders and militia alike had a gay time of it. Training Day ended with the Civil War, but it was a holiday never forgotten by those who lived through one. Many of the men of Ackerson's Company volunteered for nine months' service and served in Company A of the 22nd New Jersey Regiment during the War. Though Colonel Ackerson did not join them, he acted as head of the Committee on Volunteers, where he managed, largely through bounties, to fill the quota for the County and to prevent any draft of local men, a result which even the anti-war majority of Bergen County people could heartily applaud.

Ackerson was one of the founders of the Hackensack Gas Light Company in 1867. When the Hackensack & New York Railroad found itself in financial difficulties, it was Ackerson who was called on to step in as President to save it, which he finally did, in part by risking $60,000 of his own money to pay its losses. In short, Garret Ackerson, Jr., was one of those small-town Americans that European travelers had often remarked upon, men somewhat like English country squires except that they were not born to the position, universally respected if not universally popular, generally of good but not aristocratic lineage, who take a leading position among their fellows, whether in politics, church affairs or in business. Warmly regarded by most people, these leading citizens found themselves at odds with two groups: those who, though perhaps of greater abilities, were not at the right place at the right time, or who lacked something that inspired public confidence; and of course those others who resented anyone who rose above the dead level of his fellows. There were some in the County who felt, perhaps with cause, that their own talents exceeded those of "old Garry", and that he was singularly able to combine public affairs and his own interests, but Jersey Dutchmen were not much given to envy, and there were few indeed who did not respect and admire him. As a contemporary put it,

> ". . . He has always been a favorite with the people of Bergen County, who recognize him as one of the leading and influential men. [He is] . . . invariably courteous, dignified, friendly and sociable, [and] recognizes no dishonesty or trickery, or whatever it may be called, in any of the relations of life. . . . [Whatever may] be said about the old 'Hackensack Ring', those who look back over the years of 'old Garry's' supremacy will have to confess that the majority of men who secured state and local offices through his instrumentality were far above the average of those placed in office since. . . ." (*Hackensack Republican, December 17, 1891.*)

In seeking the Water Company charter, Judge Ackerson had named as fellow incorporators Eben Winton, Richard R. Hawkey, John H. Banta and Samuel Sneden. He had chosen well; they were all respected citizens of Hackensack, favorably known in Trenton, and pillars of the Democratic party. It may be doubted whether they had much financial interest in the water project.

Winton was the editor of the *Bergen County Democrat*, the local Bible of the party, so well established that it was commonly referred to as "The Bergen County", and an important political figure in his own right. Winton had at times probably been at some variance with Ackerson about his newspaper attacks on the Federal cause in the late War. Ackerson opposed abolition as much as Winton, but he saw the War as necessary to maintain the Union, while Winton saw it simply as a wicked and useless Abolitionist plot and was prepared to let the Union go if necessary to stop the War.

Winton had been brought to Hackensack at the outset of the Civil War to publish a paper in the interests of Bergen County's Anti-War Democratic Party, and he carried the personal journalism of the day to extremes which had not been seen in the County since Jefferson's time. He hammered away at the Lincoln administration during the War, demanding that "the Abolition nest" be routed out of Washington, along with the "thieves, swindlers and contractors who lounge around Old Abe as long as there is a dollar left in the public treasury." The few "black Republicans" of the County—there were no others in his lexicon —got even worse treatment at his hands. He minced no words in describing them as fawning patronage seekers bent on getting rich on the War. His unrelenting Democratic partisanship had continued after the War, and his enmity to local War-Democrats and Republicans abated not a whit.

Richard R. Hawkey was a well known political figure in Hackensack, about fifty years old, rough and ready in appearance, but, it was said, of a kindly disposition. He was Bergen County's jailor for many years and at times a member of its Board of Chosen Freeholders from New Barbadoes Township. He sometimes acted as a real estate agent, but was even better known as the captain of the schooner "Stewart" plying the Hackensack, where his daring navigation had earned him the reputation of the most fearless man on the river. The *Hackensack Republican* reported at the time of Ackerson's death that "the man in whom Judge Ackerson placed the greatest faith to carry out his political wishes was Captain Dick Hawkey, who possessed some of the characteristics of his chief and was too pronounced a partisan to betray the trust."

Captain Hawkey was evidently at times also connected with the Bergen Turnpike Company, as was Colonel Ackerson; at least Hawkey was often quoted in the press about the increasing number of wagons passing the toll gates. He died shortly after the Water Company charter was granted.

John H. Banta, whose firm, John H. Banta & Sons, sold "groceries, mechanics' tools, agricultural implements, wines and liquors, etc.," had held public office for many years and was an even more prominent Democrat. He was at one time Sheriff of Bergen County and frequently a delegate to State Democratic conventions. County Collector during the Civil War, Bergen's ex-soldiers remembered with pleasure his trip to Trenton in September, 1862, to pay their bounties.

Samuel Sneden, also a prominent Democrat of the village, was the Collector of New Barbadoes Township, and active in the local Methodist Church. He had been a carriage maker for more than twenty-five years and was a partner in the carriage manufacturing firm which bore the name of Sneden & DeBaun, a firm which in later years was operated by George DeBaun alone.

With such men seeking a charter, Hackensack now seemed to have every assurance that it would soon have a cheap and abundant supply of water in every house in town. There were, in fact, far more obstacles in the way of a public water supply than Garret Ackerson or anyone else imagined.

1870-1879

Though few Jersey Dutchmen could deny that the railroads, the flood of newcomers and the exploding national economy had brought an undreamed-of prosperity to Hackensack, there were many who looked back to an earlier day, when, as one of them described it,

> "The village was a place of some intelligence, excellent morals and singular uniformity in the class of its dwellings, equally removed from grandeur and squalor. There was little if any absolute poverty or ignorance, and as it was the site of a formerly famous Academy and was also seat of the Court House of the County, there were enough persons of the professions which demand a liberal education to give a decided tone of sound intelligence to the community. . . ."

Across the nation the recent war-time inflation and the huge profits of war contractors had almost destroyed business morals. Money was easy and a rosy and careless outlook prevailed. "Falling into the general way gradually and long familiar with it," one historian observes, "the better men were condoning such . . . moral standards. Many of sound conscience were intimidated, [many] silenced by prolonged experience with wrong."

Hackensack was still too much of a country town to be involved in the schemes of Jim Fisk and Jay Gould, but even in Hackensack, if land that had been worth $60 an acre a year or

27

two ago was now worth $500, why should it not be worth
$1,000 a year hence; if shares in a projected railroad, which had
been bought for $10, were worth $100, why should they not be
worth $1,000 when the railroad was completed and began to
make profits? The rumor that a new railroad was to be built, or
that the rich and powerful Englewood-based Palisades Land
Company (whose shares sold for $13,000 each and were owned
by men like President Grant and Samuel B. Tilden) was collecting acreage for a town-site, boosted land values every week, if
not oftener. In a year in which a golden spike had tied together
two oceans three thousand miles apart, who could say that
anything was impossible? The *Bergen County Democrat* freely
predicted that when all of the projected railroads were completed "the character of the County will be changed. It will become in time more than even a suburb of New York . . . it will
become a vast city in itself." In March, 1867, fifteen railroad
lobbies from Bergen County alone were attending the legislature
in Trenton. A few old fogies, and Bergen County had more than
its share, grumbled at the loose morals of the day, but even they
could not deny that virtually every one of Bergen County's ancient Dutch churches—Hackensack, North and South Schraalenburgh and Paramus—had been rebuilt and enlarged in the last
two or three years, and that new churches were springing up
all over the County. Prosperity was obviously not all bad.

As one Jersey Dutchman observed, even the critics among
his neighbors "looked about in a half-suspecting, half-cheerful
way, and soon began to spend more or less time—that could have
been more profitably employed—in keeping their ears to the
ground to discern the rumblings indicating enhanced values to
their farming lands."

If they were candid, few Bergen County people could deny
that they too were caught up in the easy money and careless
spending of the day. Nevertheless, many of them, raised in the
frugal ways of their fathers, must have been concerned about

the ostentatious display, the elegance of the new homes and dress, the brash confidence of the new men and their newly acquired wealth and even more by the stories of corruption in high places, the brazen dishonesty of the stock manipulators, the gambling and drinking at the fashionable resorts, the lavish waste of money by the new-rich people, who, as George Templeton Strong said, were "rotten and snobbish enough for any business." Strong, a member of an old and distinguished New York family, and people like him, were being elbowed aside everywhere.

All during September, 1869, Jay Gould, Jim Fisk and a few confederates—some of them very close indeed to the White House—had been buying up gold on the Exchange. As they cornered more and more of the supply, the price increased to ridiculous figures, but they held their ground, and those who had sold short were forced to cover at prices which ran up to $163.50 an ounce. Wall Street clamored for General Grant to release government gold and break Gould's and Fisk's piratical hold, but, persuaded by friends of the speculators that hard money would destroy the farmers, the Federal Government did nothing for weeks. On September 24, 1869, it finally acted, and the price of gold tumbled to a fraction of its former price. Hundreds of financiers were bankrupted. "Black Friday" is still remembered with horror on every exchange in the world. Saddest of all, it was said that Jay Gould and some of his friends, with thirty minutes' advance notice of Grant's action, had escaped with millions of dollars of profit. Rumor had it that Fisk was looking for Gould with a gun. The finances of the whole country were demoralized.

*   *   *

The autumn of 1869 was hardly a time to seek new capital for Ackerson's Hackensack Water Company, or for Voorhis' Cherry Hill Water & Gas Company either. Some of the good people of the County may have raised their eyebrows a bit when Eben

Winton had the effrontery a few weeks after Black Friday to chide the Cherry Hill Company for not going ahead, implying that his own company was only standing by to give Voorhis a chance. Under a headline "Water, Water Everywhere And Not a Drop to Drink", he wrote:

> "Whilst we, the denizens of this ancient town of Hackensack, are hardly in the condition described above, yet we are not loth to say that much of the water used in the town is not as good as could be desired. We supposed, however, that when the Cherry Hill Water Company obtained so liberal a charter as they have done to supply this town with pure and wholesome water, that there was enough enterprise in the association to have had their works built and in operation by this time. We have two chartered companies in this place having the same object in view, neither of which have made any sign thus far. Whether the one is waiting upon the other, or whether they are both somewhat timid as to the results, in view of the decided anti-improvement tendency of the so-called 'Hackensack Improvement Commission', we are not aware. Some of our people, however, have had enterprise and public spirit enough to put gas into our public streets and our houses, and let us hope that there are still others who will furnish us with water fit to use. As the Cherry Hill Water Company have taken possession of Cole's Creek, and have promised to turn that fine stream Hackensackward, we hope that the action of one or two egregious blockheads in the Hackensack Commission, in stopping of improvements, will not deter them from the prosecution of an enterprise which must eventually prove a remunerative one.
>
> "Hackensack is rapidly advancing in wealth and population in spite of old-fogyism; we have a superior quality of gas in our streets and we need pure water in our houses as well.

We cannot get along with the meager supply furnished us from our superficial wells and cisterns; what we need is a broad, liberal and gushing supply permeating through our houses, and affording every family enough and to spare for bathing as well as culinary and drinking purposes. A good bath is a luxury which cannot be too highly appreciated, but it can be obtained but in few houses in Hackensack except at the expense of much toil and trouble. Let the Cherry Hill Water Company build their works and give our peo-

G. M. Zingsem Residence, Fairmount
1876 Bergen County Atlas

ple a good supply of water, and it will pay from the start. If they do not soon move in that matter, however, the other water company will step in and take possession of their stream, *which their charter permits them to do*, build their works, and supply the town with what is badly needed— pure and wholesome water. The people will pay for the luxury and will be glad to get it by paying for it." (*Bergen County Democrat, November 12, 1869.*)

The truth was that both Ackerson and Voorhis, having recently moved into the heady business of banking, had probably put the problem of water out of their minds. Ackerson, with his Trenton connections, had obtained a state bank charter; Voorhis, with friends in Washington and Jersey City, had gotten a national bank charter and financial backing from the First National Bank of Jersey City. Both had also gotten savings bank charters, and both were too busy enlisting local support for these enterprises to worry about trying to raise money for a water company. Indeed, many people were beginning to wonder whether the water charters were going to die. Eben Winton hinted as much on February 14, 1873, when he closed a story about possible water sources with the sobering observation that "suggestions are well enough, but money is of greater importance . . ."

Other local enterprises were doing very well. The Hackensack Extension Railroad, the *New Jersey Citizen* reported (May 18, 1871), "is prospering finely as it ought, when we consider the country it passes, or the capable and gentlemanly officers who manage it." (The *New Jersey Citizen*, an exceptionally fine paper, had been founded a few months before by Cornelius Christie, another young Bergen County Dutchman of well-to-do parents who, like Charles Voorhis and W. S. Banta, had gone off to college [Yale and Harvard Law School, in his case], and then served a clerkship under the celebrated Chancellor Abraham O. Zabriskie. Unlike Voorhis and Banta, Christie remained a Democrat. After a few years as a publisher, Christie returned to the practice of law in Jersey City with considerable success. He sometimes acted as counsel for the Hackensack Water Company.)

On March 18, 1872, the first New Jersey Midland Railroad passenger train ran through Hackensack to Paterson. Hackensack people had subscribed $75,000 to bring it to town, and other liberal sums were contributed along the entire route. The opening of the road was signalized by a grand excursion to

Ellenville. Many of the people of Bergen attended the dinner that followed, where, the papers reported, Ex-Governor Price delivered "a speech of considerable length and animation."

With Ackerson and Voorhis busy promoting their banks, no one was very surprised when word went about town that Paterson interests were dickering to buy out the Hackensack Water Company charter. For their part, the people of Hackensack were not much concerned about who built a water system; they wanted water, the lack of which was only too evident when an arsonist set fire to three buildings in one night on Friday, March 6, 1873.* *The Bergen Citizen* was undoubtedly stating a simple fact when on June 20, 1873, it reported that "the leading question agitating Hackensack at present is that of a water supply and everything pertaining to it is of interest." After pointing out that

---

* A fire department had been organized in Hackensack on June 1, 1871, one fire engine being housed on State Street near the new Midland Railroad tracks, the other at DeBaun's blacksmith shop on Union Street. Experience with the two engine companies soon proved however that little confidence could be placed in them, as a story in the *Bergen County Democrat* for March 28, 1874 shows:

"Hackensack was excited over another fire this Saturday morning. This time a locomotive on the Midland set fire to the old Voorhis building opposite the Midland depot. The building was occupied by a family, named Scott, who succeeded in saving nearly all their household goods. Owing to a quarrel between the engine companies the building was badly burned before a stream of water was thrown on it. The truck companies succeeded in tearing down the greater part of the house, and this prevented the fire from spreading. We will be glad when the water works are in order, as in case of fire, hose can be attached to any hydrant, and a stream of water thrown eighty feet high. This will do away with the engine companies which have been a source of annoyance and expense ever since they were purchased. We had hoped that the respectable men in these two companies would have taken the matter in hand before this, and have expelled the rowdy element which is such a source of disturbance. They have not done so, and our citizens therefore condemn the two companies."

the Ackerson charter would be void if work was not commenced by March 12, 1874, the *Citizen* went on to report that:

> "This last charter is the one that General Hoxey, of Paterson, desires to get possession of, and if he does so he offers to build the necessary works. We understand that G. Ackerson, Jr., is willing to transfer his right, and so perhaps are the other incorporators. General Hoxey proposes to allow the citizens of Hackensack to take all the stock they wish, and he will take the balance if there is any. He will complete the works before Fall, taking the water from the Hackensack River near River Edge, and building a reservoir there on a hill 70 feet above the tide water. If this offer is accepted no expense will be incurred by the town, nor by anyone who does not use the water.
>
> "The proposal of Mr. Hoxey seems to be a practical method of solving the water question, and we understand that a majority of the members of the Improvement Commission are strong advocates of it, and none of them opposed to it. . . .
>
> "We trust that the present agitation may have some valuable practical results, and that while the interests of the town may be at all times duly guarded from any harm, no opportunity will be missed to secure for it what it so much needs as an adequate supply of water for all emergencies." *(New Jersey Citizen, June 20, 1873.)*

The people of Hackensack had little use for Paterson—the *Bergen County Democrat* had once observed that some ancient willows in front of the Dutch Church were "sound in appearance, but as rotten as Paterson"—but help from any quarter was welcome. General Thomas D. Hoxey was a sixty-year-old lawyer, a man who had made some money in the cotton manufacturing business before studying law and entering politics in Paterson, where he made a small name for himself as supporter

of "greenback" causes. His military title derived from a Briga-
dier General's commission in the prewar militia, for, though he
was, as a contemporary said, "a man of wonderful energy and
vigor, strong in his likes and dislikes . . . always opposed to
slavery [and] loathed tobacco and intoxicating liquor in any
form," he was too old to take part in the late War. Of far more
importance in the circumstances, General Hoxey was the head
of the Passaic Water Company, and in fact seems to have done
its engineering work as well as its legal and financial work, and
was thus a likely candidate for the task of laying out and building Hackensack's new supply.

With the prospect of at least one person who would put up
the necessary money if local people failed, Ackerson and John
H. Banta advertised on July 10, 1873,

"HACKENSACK WATER CO. Books for subscription
to the capital stock of the Hackensack Water Co., will be
opened at the office of Garret Ackerson, Jr., on Monday,
Tuesday and Wednesday, next, July 14th, 15th and 16th,
from nine, A.M., until three, P.M.

> Garret Ackerson, Jr., } Commissioners
> John H. Banta, }
>
> Hackensack, July 10, 1873"

The *Democrat* added an editorial word to spur local investors:

"Water! Water!

"For months the cry of water has been on the tongues of
our citizens, and by reference to our advertising columns a
notice will be found asking for subscriptions to the stock
of the Hackensack Water Company. If sufficient stock is
taken, this town will be supplied with water from the
Hackensack sufficient to supply a town of 50,000 inhabitants. General Hoxey offers to put the whole machinery in

working order for $100,000, and if the people of this town do not see fit to subscribe to the stock, he will take the whole amount himself. It is proposed to locate the works on the Hackensack, a few miles above town, and it is claimed on account of the altitude of the proposed reservoir, a stream can be thrown over the highest building in town from a hydrant. Every property holder should take some stock, as an enterprise like this ought not to fail for want of subscriptions. Let those who have asked for water so urgently now come forward and choose what they will do." *(Bergen County Democrat, July 11, 1873)*

When the books were opened, to the consternation of Ackerson, Winton, and their partners, instead of General Hoxey, their arch-rival Charles H. Voorhis came in and subscribed for the controlling interest in the company. Voorhis evidently saw that if he wanted to build a water system, the Ackerson charter was far better than his own limited Cherry Hill charter. He had used Hoxey as a stalking horse to get Garry Ackerson to put it up for sale. Relations between Ackerson and Voorhis were scrupulously correct, as befitted dignified Jersey Dutchmen, but no one doubted that Garret Ackerson would have put up the money himself if he had known who was trying to take over the enterprise.

Once he had gotten the charter Voorhis proceeded with great energy to build the water system. He brought in one of New Jersey's ablest engineering and construction firms, Bacot & Ward, of Jersey City, and they wasted no time in getting to work. Before long, Main Street was a network of trenches and service connections. R. C. Bacot, the head of the construction firm, was the first of a long line of distinguished engineers that the Hackensack Water Company is proud to claim as its own. Born of a prominent Huguenot family of Charleston, South Carolina, in 1818, he graduated from the University of South

Carolina at the age of 17 and commenced an engineering career that lasted sixty years. In a day when railroad routes were laid out by pioneers who rode through untracked forests on horseback seeking the best grades, he went out to explore for railroad rights-of-way in the back country of Kentucky, the Carolinas

New Jersey Midland Railroad Train
at Jersey City Terminal, c. 1880
Walter A. Lucas Collection

and Tennessee, and, later, in New Hampshire and Massachusetts. He moved to Jersey City in 1839, at the age of 21, when that place had a population of a few thousand (by 1870 it had grown to a population of over one hundred thousand), and there almost singlehandedly laid out most of the streets and other improvements. As an architect, he designed most of its early public buildings, schools, churches and jails, as well as many private dwellings. He was entrusted with spending millions of dollars to purchase several railroad rights-of-way to the Hudson waterfront. He was later in charge of Jersey City's water system for a time and was credited with introducing water meters for large consumers, a plan later adopted by New

York City and other public systems. He was elected to the Assembly several times, and held many other appointive offices where his engineering skill was needed, including a post as a commissioner to establish the boundary between the States of New York and New Jersey. It is easy to credit a contemporary's statement that he "made a more pronounced impression upon the physical development of [Jersey City] than any other resident during more than fifty years."

*   *   *

A few months after Charles Voorhis took over control of the Water Company, commuters debarking at the Essex Street Station brought news of a Wall Street panic that seemed to have little to do with Hackensack, however excited the commuters were about it. It was, in point of fact, the most important thing that Hackensack had heard since the news of Fort Sumter. Friday, September 18, 1873, was one of all too many "Black Fridays" in American history, a day-long panic in Wall Street which began in the morning with the announcement that the banking house of Jay Cooke & Company had suspended payments because it had been unable to sell the Northern Pacific bonds it had recently underwritten.

"The announcement that Jay Cooke & Co. had been compelled to suspend payment," Harpers Weekly reported, "shattered all confidence, and the panic became a general riot. Wall Street was the scene of wild excitement all day." The fact that Jay Cooke was perhaps the most respected financier in America, untouched by the scandals of the day and guilty of no wrongdoing, made the case worse. Stocks plunged immediately, people seemed to come from nowhere to fill Broad Street and Wall Street with milling mobs. The financial community was in panic.

On Saturday commuters brought even worse news. The Stock Exchange had been forced to close after two hours, and twenty of Wall Street's leading firms had closed their doors. Worse than that, the Union Trust Company, on the corner of Broadway and Rector Street, had also suspended payments when the Lake Shore Railroad defaulted on a call loan for $1,750,000, and the panic was renewed in a more alarming and disastrous form. Some of the solid citizens of Hackensack passed this off as another example of the excesses and greed of the financial world, proof that those who lived by speculation would reap their own harvest.

Most of the public, the government and the press were unanimous in their reaction to the stock market disaster. They were sure that the economy of the country was sound and that the real business of the country would not be affected, whatever might happen to stock speculators, who deserved exactly what they got. The *Democrat* put the feelings of most people about as well as anyone, when it wrote on September 24, six days after the crash, that:

> "The legitimate business of the County has now been tested in the severe crucible of a new panic, and it has not only stood the trial, but it has been unshaken. . . . The waves of panic have surged against all business for nearly one week, and all legitimate channels have stood like the rock-ribbed shore, everything outside of purely speculative avenues is serene and healthy, and the wealth, the products and the substantial resources of the whole country never were greater than now. . . ."

The *Harpers Weekly* story on October 4, 1873, two weeks later, was almost a paraphrase of the *Democrat's* observations. The reactions of the public, the government and the press, were, of course, precisely wrong.

The real business of the country may or may not have been sound, but it could not stand after its financial and credit supports had been destroyed. Indeed, many felt that more than finance and credit was involved, that decay ran through all of society, and there was all too much evidence that they were right. Preachers like Henry Ward Beecher were better known for their scandalous private reputations than for their sermons. Under the prevailing elective system, George Templeton Strong observed, most of the judges in New York would have appeared to better advantage as prisoners before the dock of General Sessions than on the bench of the Supreme Court; indeed that is exactly where a few like Barnard and Cardoza soon found themselves. People were more incensed at their legislators for selling their votes below the going rate, and thus disgracing their districts, than for the practice itself. Newspapers that prated sagely of the wickedness of Jay Gould and Jim Fisk— the latter now dead at the hands of Edward S. Stokes for his affair with Josie Mansfield—were too often as corrupt as the robber barons they attacked. The opinions of James Gordon Bennett, publisher of the *New York Herald*, one historian has said, "always loosely held, were to be had by the shrewdest person and that one who had most to give in flattery and attention, if not in other kinds of gain." Bennett was by no means the only publicist who was at the beck and call of any public figure who gave him the attention he considered a press lord's due; in point of fact he was one of the few who preferred attention to hard cash. Of the honest publishers, many were so blatantly partisan that none but fools believed their reports.

Democrats had every reason to hold up their hands in horror at General Grant's connections with dishonest stock speculators and shifty politicians, every reason, that is, but that they themselves were opportunists of the grossest kind, men like Horace Greeley and Horatio Seymour, whose principles of the morning changed by sundown. Even the now-pious Samuel J. Tilden had become rich in the high councils of the Tweed Ring before he discovered that Tweed was not really a civic reformer, and, worse, that any connection with him was not likely to forward the ambitions of a moralizing Presidential candidate.

On the other hand, the evidence of the corruption of an age may be too available, too dramatic. Was the society that built the transcontinental railroads, that financed and built billions of dollars of transportation, utility and industrial enterprises, that virtually invented the techniques of mass production, that began the national distribution of consumer goods—was that society really the society of Jim Fisk, Edward Stokes and Josie Mansfield, or was it the society of George Westinghouse, Jay Cooke, Thomas Edison, Alexander Graham Bell, George Pullman and Cyrus McCormick? Was the Panic of 1873 and the seven-year depression that followed the penalty for the decadence of the age, or was it a failure of one element in a new and infinitely complicated mechanism that no one understood, a failure that set up a seven-year chain of stresses and failures of otherwise sound parts? Only the simplistic moralists, the greenbackers and the grangers, and their latter-day counterparts, have been sure. The record tells us little but that the nation's business, which had taken a great leap forward after the War, came to a halt and did not move again for years; and that the burdens of the panic fell on humble workmen, honest businessmen and upright financiers who had little part in the excesses for which the age has become known.

For a time things seemed to go on as usual in Hackensack. To most people not connected with the stock market or New York's large banks and not dependent on credit to finance their speculations, the Wall Street panic seemed no problem of theirs. Unfortunately, the truth was that Hackensack was almost as much involved in the national economy as Wall Street, and would suffer for it. Even before work commenced on the water system, this was borne home to Bergen County. Within two months after the stock market collapse, the papers reported that the Midland Railroad was near bankruptcy, with employees making voluntary donations of their back pay to try to keep the road going. At the end of January 1874, Bergen County saw a new spectacle, tax sales—

"There was great excitement on Wednesday in regard to the sales for taxes—it being the first that ever occurred in this village. Crowds filled the Sheriff's Office and the Mansion House. The novelty of the affair created much interest." *(Bergen County Democrat, January 30, 1874.)*

The novelty soon wore off, for the first sales were merely a few raindrops before the storm, and by March 1874 even the papers stopped pretending that everything was fundamentally all right in Bergen County.

"Along the lines of the New York and Oswego Midland Railroad, there is destitution and want. Hundreds of families are actually in want. Hundreds of men have worked faithfully several months on that line of railroad for the company and have been put off from month to month without pay, and at last discharged. They are out of clothes and money. They are unable to obtain further credit—they are surrounded by starving families and there is no help for them." *(Bergen County Democrat, March 20, 1874.)*

Despite the hard times, Charles Voorhis pushed ahead with the waterworks system. The engineering plan was simple. North of the village of Hackensack, John C. Zabriskie's farm in Cherry Hill stood on the high hill not far from the Hackensack River which had given the settlement its name. It had been called Brower's Hill during the Revolution, when it held American defense works, and it was now usually called Zabriskie's Hill, after the family that had owned it for generations. The plan was to build a huge brick reservoir on the top of this elevation and to pump water up from the river through an intake on the Lozier place, just to the east, and let it flow down from the reservoir into the village of Hackensack by gravity. Mr. Zabriskie was reluctant to sell any of his land, but Mr. Voorhis finally acquired enough for a reservoir, which stood there well into modern times, though long since abandoned for water supply purposes, the bottom filled with cat-tails and rushes. The decision to pump water from the river at Cherry Hill is something of a mystery, because the river was brackish if not salt for several miles above the intake, and an alternate fresh-water source was at hand in Cole's Brook, just south of the hill. Perhaps the surface of the river was always fresh in 1874, when the tree-covered watershed levelled off the river flow; perhaps it was fresh during certain tides, and all pumping was done then. Whatever the reason, there is every evidence that the people of Hackensack found the water pure and wholesome; in fact they often boasted that it was better than New York City's Croton water.

In a quiet way they were very partial to the river that flowed along the eastern boundary of their town. One local writer was almost poetic about it:

> "The stream is marked by long reaches of smooth water; by graceful curves in its shore lines; by broad and beautiful bays and by clustered islands. Here and there its shores are bold, and jutting down to the water's edge, are reflected in the calm surface of the stream. Over its waters glide, in the long summer days and evenings, row boats and sail boats . . . bearing fishermen intent on securing their daily supplies from the finny tribes beneath; or merry parties going picknicking to some favorite nooks along the shore, or gentlemen giving their friends from the City an outing upon the placid stream.
> . . . For pleasure in summer, when the fleecy clouds are mirrored in the waters below, or for sport in winter, when

Boating on Hackensack River
Post Card Collection of Mr. Gerry de la Ree

the skaters skim over its frozen surface, or for profit, when the fishermen and sailors utilize the stream and its tides, the river is highly appreciated, and it adds greatly to the beauty and attractiveness of the town, and to the enjoyment of its citizens." *(Bergen County Democrat History of Hackensack, pp. 72, 73.)*

On February 24, 1874, the *Bergen Index* reported that "The Water Co. has spent nearly $50,000 in laying pipes from Essex Street to within 1500 feet of the proposed reservoir location. Before May 1, $20,000 more will be spent." Commissioners were about to be appointed to appraise the value of the land taken by condemnation for the project. Spring and summer turned to fall and the men were still down in trenches digging their way along the streets, putting in iron pipes and connecting service lines to the new customers, though some of the more conservative people of the town, who had been drinking

44

well water for years, saw no reason to change to river water, whatever outsiders told them about the pollution of shallow wells.

The workmen were not helped by the weather during the spring of 1874, which, the papers said, "like the present generation, has degenerated and become unstable, and not to be relied on." On May 1, 1874, Hackensack had a twelve-inch fall of snow, several weeks later than the celebrated snowfall of fifty years before, when farmers came to a large auction at Campbell's Tavern in sleighs and found themselves bogged down in mud and slush when it turned warm on the way home. On August 25, the *New Jersey Citizen* reported that "the Water Co. expects to lay pipes this week in Main Street. The reservoir is finished and will be pumped full today." By early October workmen were busy laying pipes in lower Main Street, but there was still a good deal of work left to be done further to the north. On Tuesday, October 20th, the day before the scheduled start of service, the *New Jersey Citizen* reported that "laying water pipes in town will be finished this week."

Finally the great day came and the water flowed. The report of the *Citizen* was so full of detail that one can almost see the fountain on the Green sparkling in the afternoon sun, the rows on rows of uniformed firemen and the top-hatted dignitaries:

"WATER CELEBRATION
"A Fine Day and a Large Turn-out of Citizens
—The Fountain.

"Wednesday, [October 21, 1874] was a bright and most memorable day in the history of Hackensack. For some time past, as our readers are aware, the Fire Department had been making preparations which culminated in a glorious result.

"About noon the fountain on the Public Green began to play, then the crowd began slowly to collect, and then the bands of music and fire companies, with gallant Company C, put in an appearance. G. Ackerson, Jr., D. A. Pell, R. P. Terhune, mounted on spirited steeds as marshals, rode up and down gathering the constituents of the procession. At about 2 o'clock, the line having been formed, an interesting presentation scene took place in an open carriage containing a few distinguished guests, in front of the Hackensack House. Chas. H. Voorhis, Esq., in behalf of Messrs. Bacot & Ward, the contractors, addressing himself to Hon. J. J. Anderson, the president of the Hackensack Commission, presented to the citizens of Hackensack the handsome fountain on the Public Green as a memorial of the introduction of water into town.

"In reply, President Anderson said that this was the first celebration of the kind in Hackensack, and that the people should feel proud of the water and grateful to the gentlemen who had originated the enterprise. It needed support, and the people should give it freely and fully. The company had done what the town could not. He took pleasure in receiving . . . the beautiful fountain now playing in the park. About 2:30 P.M. the procession started in the following order. Garret Ackerson, Jr., Marshal, mounted. Sheriff Pell and R. P. Terhune, Assistant Marshals, mounted. Next came a brass band and a company of militia, followed by David Ackerman's beautiful barouche, containing the following members of the Water Co.: John H. Banta, President; C. H. Voorhis; A. D. Brower; J. C. Quackenbush; J. P. Westervelt [Brower was Secretary; the last two were probably directors], Hackensack Improvement Commission; J. J. Anderson, President; G. J. Ackerman, Secretary and Treasurer; Commissioner Jacobson. [A carriage filled with local notables was next, followed by a dozen brass bands and firemen's groups; then followed A. W. Christie's stage with twenty men, and ten or twelve private carriages.] "In all, about 325 men participated in the parade. The following was the line of march: Through Main to Hudson, Hudson to Hoboken Ave.; Hoboken Ave. to Lafayette St.; Lafayette St. to Hudson, to Essex, to Union, to Cottage Place, to State, to Berry, to Union, to Ward, to Park, to Bogert, to Main, to Bergen, where the parade was dismissed at 4 P.M. A bountiful collation was spread and awaiting all the invited guests in the engine and truck houses. Ample justice was done to the feast by the hungry heroes of the day.

Fountain Presented by Bacot & Ward
upon Commencement of Water Service October 21, 1874
Post Card Collection of Mr. Gerry de la Ree

"SIDELIGHTS

"There was a generous display of bunting along the entire route, all the public buildings, prominent business houses and many private dwellings being handsomely trimmed and decorated with the national colors.

"Young America being greatly excited and anxious to witness the proceedings of the day, Prof. Haas and Prof. Ryder wisely closed the public schools under their charge, thus giving their scholars a treat that will be their favorite theme for many a day. . . .

"The dignitaries of the town assembled in the parlors of the Hackensack House after the parade, and numerous toasts were given and responded to.

"For hours after the parade, and until past 8 o'clock, the people were treated to frequent music by the different bands, but mainly by The Washington Brass Band of New York City, which serenaded ex-Judge Chas. H. Voorhis in the evening, he having originated and organized the Water Company by his indomitable energy under circumstances which would have caused many men to have abandoned it. Mr. Voorhis invited the entire band into his residence, where they were wined to their satisfaction.

"The streets were alive with people until a late hour, everyone seeming to consider it a day of jubilee and accordingly went in for enjoyment.

"The weather was all that could be desired. A dash of rain in the morning was soon followed by a clear sky, and the afternoon was of spring-like sweetness. The slight sprinkling just nicely laid the dust for marching.

"In honor of the occasion the base of the fountain and the outer rim of the ground basin were ornamented by Gamewell Bros. with plants from their fine collection.

"The scene on and around the Green on the disbanding of the procession—with the red-shirted firemen, the neatly uniformed soldier boys, the bands with their burnished instruments, the ladies in their fall costumes, citizens in various dress, the playing fountain, and the mellow sunlight

48

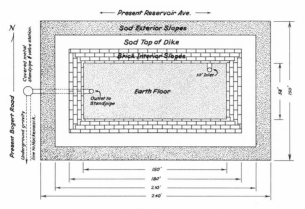

Reconstruction of Plan of Cherry Hill Reservoir
Prepared by Harold B. Zabriskie.
Mr. Zabriskie was Born and Raised on the
old Zabriskie Farm Where the Reservoir Stood

flooding all, was gaily picturesque." *(New Jersey Citizen,
October 23, 1874.)*

The irony of Colonel Ackerson's acting as grand marshal of
the ceremonies after he had failed to build the system, we may
be sure, was not lost on the bystanders, nor the courtesy of
Charles Voorhis, who had succeeded, both of them dignified,
cheerful and self-possessed in any situation, but there were many
who joined in the Water Day celebration whose mood hardly
fitted the gala atmosphere. The Panic of 1873 had not ended
by October 1874; in point of fact it was not to end for six or
seven more years, and business was to get far worse before it
got better. At first, the Water Company seemed relatively untouched by the holocaust. The *New Jersey Citizen* for January 15, 1875, carried a long technical article by Professor
Albert R. Leeds of Stevens Institute pointing out that the
Hackensack River would easily provide 20,000,000 gallons a
day, enough to supply the City of Hoboken and provide for

thirty years growth. The Hackensack Water Company charter, he said, would be an ideal vehicle for such a system. When the *Citizen* for February 16, 1875, carried a story that the charter had been supplemented to permit it to supply "all that part of Bergen County which lies east and south of the Saddle River" many readers surmised that Charles Voorhis had larger plans for his new company than to supply the forty-five hundred people of Hackensack.

Others in the County were suffering badly from the depression. Many farmers who had expected to live for the rest of their lives in affluence on the interest from mortgages they had received from land speculators had already returned to their farms to mend their fences, plow down five years of growth of weeds and underbrush and begin farm life over again. Storekeepers closed once-flourishing businesses. Between November 1875 and June 1876, no trains at all ran on the Jersey City and Albany, and continued service on other local railroads was a chancey thing.

In Hackensack Township (Englewood, Teaneck, Bergenfield, Dumont) the Poor House was filled to overflowing and the treasury was so empty that the Township Committee had to ask the local churches to keep public charges from starving. Carpenters were lucky to get jobs as farm laborers at $1.00 a day. As one man said, if a tribe of Indians were to settle on the abandoned properties of the Palisades Land Company they would not be disturbed.

In March, 1875, the New Jersey Midland found itself unable to pay its debts, and its creditors moved to appoint a receiver. The *Democrat*, which had been following the troubles of its train crews for the last few months, was obliged to report on March 1 that the road had cancelled its mail train, "thus throwing out of employment one of the oldest and most popular conductors on the road, David Blauvelt, who had run the first through train over the road." "David," the paper added, "leaves the company with seven months' pay due him." The railroad's bankruptcy was blamed for the lay-off of hundreds of workmen at the Rogers Locomotive Works in Paterson. The railroad had had its share of troubles even before the stock market crash. On April 10, 1872, one of its trains went through the Saddle River Bridge with twenty-five people aboard, all of whom except the brakeman fortunately escaped death. A few months later low bridges in Jersey City sheared three smokestacks off its locomotives and on September 26, 1873, an eight-minute error in a conductor's watch brought death to three men in a collision of a freight train and a passenger train near Wortendyke.

In October, 1875, there were 82 tax sales in Harrington township alone, and by 1876 the number in the County ran into the thousands. "It would astonish the hewers of wood and drawers of water," the *Democrat* wrote, "to see the patrician names which figure in the list of delinquent taxpayers . . . who are now paying 12 per cent interest to the Township. . . ." From time to time the papers printed optimistic stories of a turn, but the depression continued unabated, and those who had bought land at high prices were being harder pinched every day.

Politics, which often seemed to be Hackensack's chief occupation, went on as usual, however. The Hayes-Tilden contest in 1876, and the subsequent controversy over the election, brought partisan politics to a fever pitch. Charles H. Voorhis, the Republican nominee for Congress, went down to defeat in the 1876 elections. The *Democrat*, which always predicted Republican defeats, had predicted the outcome when he was nominated:

"Judge Charles H. Voorhis, of Hackensack has been elected as the victim. Mr. Voorhis is a representative Republican, comes from old Bergen stock, and if he can't talk Dutch quite as well as his father, has many qualities which ought to commend the Republican strength. He will receive some opposition from certain active Republicans in Hackensack, but Judge Charles has a way of whipping them in which will secure their votes, even if they dislike their nominee. He will be beaten, however, in the district by a large majority."

In 1878, when he was nominated again, the *Democrat* once more opened its guns on him, at first with a few light touches, reporting on October 4th that he was

"having a chimney put on the [Water Company] steam engine at Cherry Hill. By this means it is presumed that it is intended to deluge the Congressional district. Water is a powerful element, but in this case it will require something besides water to moisten the way."

A few days before the election it became openly partisan:

"On the other hand, we have Mr. Charles H. Voorhis. Mr. Voorhis, socially, is a gentleman. Politically, - - - well! the Judge was once a Democrat. He left the Democratic party - - - and for some years past has led the Republican party to defeat. Mr. Voorhis has several times been a candidate for public office but his fellowmen thought too much of him to expose him to the temptations of office, and consequently let him remain at home. There could be many things said about Mr. Voorhis which would not commend him to the suffrages of his party, but it is with his political record with which we have to deal. He represents the Republican party in its worse and better element. . . ."

The *Democrat* went on to make it clear that what it really objected to was Voorhis' belief that Hayes was legally elected. "No Democrat in this County can consistently vote for him," it said, "and we don't believe they will." The *Democrat* was wrong. Charles Voorhis received a substantial majority of the votes, and took his seat in Congress. Neither the *Democrat* nor the voters of the County knew that Voorhis was far more worried about the desperate state of his business affairs than he was about the *Democrat's* political attacks. It had been a foolhardy thing to build a water system in the depths of a depression, and equally foolhardy to open a new bank in such times. His own property holdings were unsaleable, and taxes and mortgage interest were piling up against them. The Hackensack Water Company had been trying to sell $500 bonds carrying seven per cent interest free of tax, with no success even at a 10% discount. Few water customers were paying their bills, and many others had discontinued service. Even the Hackensack Improvement Commission, whose treasury was so empty that it could not pay one creditor's bill for $3.24, was obliged to default in its hydrant rents.

Reserved, dignified and seemingly successful, Voorhis kept his troubles to himself. As the *Democrat* itself had said in one of its few friendly articles about Judge Voorhis ". . . the old families of Bergen County are, for the most part, puzzles to the ordinary observer. They do not wear their hearts upon their sleeves for daws to peck at. . . ."

By March, 1879, he could hold on no longer, and, without warning, the Water Company publicly admitted that it could not pay its debts. The *Democrat* for April 4th reported that the Honorable A. A. Hardenburgh of Jersey City had been appointed its receiver at the suit of Bacot & Ward, the contractors who built the system. It was the first of a chain of misfortunes that struck Charles Voorhis. He had pushed forward, even after the depression began, believing, like everyone else, that it would soon end and that his properties would regain their value. He managed for several years to keep his ventures out of bankruptcy, but when one of the props of his finances fell it was inevitable that they would all go. In October, 1879, he conceded that he could no longer meet his own debts as they accrued, and made an assignment for creditors. The *Democrat* for October 31, 1879, reported that he listed his liabilities at $301,000; the value of his assets, which once was thought to be over $1,000,000, being uncertain. It went on,

> "The failure is a very bad one, and besides carrying down Mr. Voorhis and family it inflicts serious injury on many of his friends. The most bitter enemy of Mr. Voorhis cannot but pity the sad plight he and his family are in at the present moment. [Since the First National Bank was almost wholly a Voorhis enterprise, the *Democrat* thought it wise to add:] The Bank Examiner, Mr. Young, authorizes us to say that depositors in the Hackensack Bank will receive their deposits in full. There is no need for hurrying, and his advice to depositors is to keep cool. The bank is ably prepared to settle. When the depositors are paid in full, the stock of the bank will be worth about 50 per cent."

The Examiner was obviously trying to stop a run on the bank, but his optimism was hardly justified by the facts. Though several efforts were made by local people to put new life into the institution, its affairs were too tangled and its assets too impaired by the depression to recover, and it soon closed its doors. Depositors ultimately received only a small fraction of their money. Its accounts and the accounts of the Water Company were in complete disarray. Charles Voorhis had evidently long since ceased to try to keep the records of his affairs straight and he steadfastly refused to discuss them.

To anyone who remembers the great depression of the 1930's, the story of Charles H. Voorhis is all too familiar. Convinced that his holdings were worth a million dollars or more, he first put off one creditor to pay another, then shifted the assets of one enterprise to another enterprise to cover some temporary trouble, next dipped into some dormant estate rather than let a hundred thousand dollar business go bankrupt for the lack of a ready thousand dollars, then bolstered one company by bank loans and issued bonds of another company to cover the bank's loan losses, probably all in the belief that he was protecting investors, the bank depositors and the beneficiaries of estates from immediate liquidation; moreover, in the firm assurance that his own assets would make up any deficiency if an ultimate loss ensued. When his land holdings, the bank, the Water Company and his other enterprises went down deeper into the mire of depression he was trapped by his expedients. When it became obvious that his own assets would not cover his deficits, he turned to more and more desperate measures, for it was now his own and his family's good name that was at stake, his brilliant professional and political career, his high position as a churchman, indeed, everything he stood for. It would be easy enough after the fact to say that he should not have taken the first step from the straight and narrow path. Only those who have lived through such a holocaust know the conviction, a conviction that moves even honest men, that if one can somehow live through the day, things will be better tomorrow, that any expedient is justifiable to solve the immediate problem; in short, that if for want of a nail a Kingdom will be lost, it is only right to beg, borrow or steal the nail.

In this, men who have no reputation to save, men who have but recently come to the surface, who have no capital and little capacity, men under no pretense of being anything but unprincipled rascals, have the advantage over their betters. They can shrug their shoulders at their creditors, wipe out their indebtedness, go elsewhere and start over again. Charles Voorhis was a prisoner of his own good name. If he had been able to admit failure earlier, he could have salvaged most of his property. As it was, he had to hide his troubles until they destroyed him.

And destroy him they did. His subsequent misfortunes are almost too painful to catalog: friends gone, a brilliant professional career blasted; reduced to drawing papers for lawyers who were not fit to carry his briefcase; his household furniture sold under his family's eyes; his distinguished and beloved father dead in disgrace as a result of his own moves to protect his son; indictments, trials and public abuse; brave attempts to salvage something by his legal talents; equally pitiful efforts to stand up in quiet dignity despite his mistakes; removal to a small flat in Hoboken, and finally death by his own hand, an envelope nearby marked for his ailing wife, with $5 in it, all of the money he had in the world.

Providence raised up Charles H. Voorhis quickly and threw him down harshly. Three-quarters of a century after his death we can let his misfortunes lie buried in his grave and remember him only as the valedictorian of Rutgers' Class of 1853; the brilliant, handsome young lawyer; the friend of Abraham Lincoln; the man who helped to establish municipal government in the City of Hackensack; the man who founded one of its principal churches, who brought its schools into the modern age and paved its main streets, and, as we have seen, the man who built Bergen County's first water system.

1880-1889

Abram A. Hardenburgh, the receiver of the Water Company, kept it in operation as best he could despite great obstacles, not the least of which was the reluctance of the Commissioners of Hackensack to pay their hydrant charges, possibly from a simple desire to attract votes, possibly from the common misunderstanding that hydrant fees represent an exorbitant charge for the use of a relatively low-priced hydrant fixture, without taking into account the costs of the larger pipes, reservoirs and pumps necessary to make the fixture useful. (A great part of the cost of a water system would be eliminated if there were no need for fire service.) Of course, it is also possible that the Commissioners simply did not have the money.

By 1880 the Water Company had been acquired by Bacot & Ward, the engineers and contractors who built the system and the holders of a large number of bonds taken in payment for its construction. They formed a new company, the Hackensack Water Company Reorganized, with William S. Banta as President, John F. Ward as Secretary and R. C. Bacot as Treasurer. People with long memories observed with interest that Garret Ackerson, the original incorporator, was one of the two outside directors in the new group. Mr. Ackerson, though still a respected figure in town, had suffered considerably in local prestige when his own bank, like Charles Voorhis', was closed by the depression, and his political power was no longer what it had been.

Northwest part of the Green, Hackensack, c. 1908
Bergen County Historical Society

Mr. B. A. Cleveland was named engineer of the pumping
works at $50 per month and Mr. C. J. Westervelt was con-
tinued as superintendent and collector at $25 a month. "Var-
ious improvements will be made in the management of the
works," the *Democrat* said in reporting the reorganization, "and
the prospects are that the affairs of the company will be conducted satisfactorily." The Company published a new sched-
ule of rates and advertised that the Superintendent "would be
at its office on Main Street, opposite Washington Mansion
House, on Thursday of each week for collections and information." The water was evidently pumped only as needed to fill
the reservoir. A report from the man in charge shows that the
pumps were worked only eighteen hours during the week of
November 20 to 27, 1880, when 752,000 gallons were pumped,

"using 23 Barrows of Cole Each 160 pounds, and will not pump until December 6, 1880." The 50,000 gallons per day sent out during those two weeks has since grown nearly two thousand times.

Business did not proceed without troubles. In May, 1881, the main transmission line through Fairmount burst, "flooding the roadway, besides inconveniencing our people wonderfully. The water motor in the *Democrat* office was quiet, and as a result, we were compelled to ask the aid of the *Republican* in getting out our edition." Water motors were not very satisfactory sources of power. (It had been proposed to use a water motor to power the new pipe organ at the Reformed Church, but there is no record of its performance.) Between line breaks and motor failures, the Water Company got more than its share of publicity for the *Democrat's* troubles with water-powered presses.

The Water Company officials, however, had something on their minds besides the complaints of the *Democrat*. They were negotiating for a ten-year contract to supply water to the City of Hoboken, calling for payment to the Company of $75,000 a year, a project that would involve millions of dollars of capital and a complete change of the source of supply from Cherry Hill to a point further up the river.

Hoboken at that time, a contemporary wrote,

> "with its 30,000 population . . . possesses all of the con-
> veniences of much larger cities, together with a location
> unrivalled by any. . . . Throughout its whole area there
> are abundant evidences of the enterprise of her citizens in
> her massive buildings and impressive residences. The streets
> of the city are well paved and in good condition. . . . It
> is the terminus of the Delaware, Lackawanna and Western,
> . . . and the very superior harbor has attracted a number

of foreign steamship lines, which now have their docks and facilities here. . . . Hoboken is largely populated by those engaged in business in New York City, who find that the cost of living is much less in the smaller city, and, at the same time, suffer none of the inconveniences."

A large part of the land in the City was owned by the Hoboken Land and Improvement Company, incorporated in 1838 by the famous Stevens family, descendants of John Stevens of Hoboken (1749-1838), capitalist, inventor and statesman, the man who designed and built the first locomotive in America and the inverted "T" rail which is now in universal use, and the chief promoter of the Camden & Amboy Railroad and several others, who designed and built many early steamboats and financed many early American enterprises. The Hoboken Land Company and the Stevens family were undoubtedly the prime movers in bringing Hackensack water to Hoboken. At the Company's annual meeting on June 7, 1881, the directors entertained a number of gentlemen from Hoboken, who made an inspection of the works and capacity of the Company. After looking over the property, the *Democrat* reported, "they adjourned to the Mansion House, where Mr. Cronkright had in waiting a collation, which was speedily stored away under many a capacious vest. The Hoboken officials expressed themselves as highly pleased with the project, and it only needs proper management to give Hoboken all the pure Hackensack water it requires." The new directors elected at the 1881 meeting included Garret A. Hobart, who had successfully revived the New Jersey Midland Railroad, and later became Vice President of the United States.

There was a certain amount of controversy in Hoboken about shifting to the Hackensack River source. One opponent of the plan solemnly informed the Hoboken Water Commissioners that the Hackensack River was dry a short distance above the pump house of the Water Company. The Commissioners could hardly be blamed for believing it, because the summer had been the hottest and driest in the memory of living men. The temperature reached 106° in Hackensack early in September, a record for the century, and many streams were actually dry. "On Sunday, [the *Democrat* wrote,] the Commissioners drove from Hoboken to the alleged place where the river had run dry and found fifteen feet, with the tide coming in, and a large schooner sailing along several miles above the pumping house. . . . Hoboken people needn't feel uneasy about

Hoboken River Front in 1881
Industries of New Jersey

their water supply." The *Democrat* went on to say that the rumor was that the Stevens' Estate had taken $300,000 of the stock of the Water Company, and that the prospect of enlarging the plant was good. In September 1881, Hoboken awarded a formal contract to the Company, to take effect November 1, 1882, and the action was confirmed by an almost unanimous popular vote at the ensuing election in November. The Village of Hackensack also welcomed the move—the drought had made everyone water conscious—because it meant that a new and enlarged plant would be constructed in the fresh water reaches of the river, and that sufficient capital would be provided to extend service throughout the town, where many people had recently been forced to pay for their own private lines to reach the few principal mains.

The Bacot and Ward interests, not having the large capital resources necessary to complete a line to Hoboken, had negotiated a contract to sell the Company on condition that the Hoboken contract was granted. Immediately after the referendum, on November 9, 1881, the Board was reorganized, with W. W. Shippen, Daniel Runkle, Julian H. Kean and Robert W. deForest taking the places of the Bacot and Ward representatives. Mr. R. C. Bacot himself tendered his resignation, but was asked to continue as President and director.

Mr. W. W. Shippen was executor of the Stevens Estate and representative of the Stevens family interests. Mr. Shippen died in 1885 and was succeeded by Mr. Edwin A. Stevens, his brother-in-law, whose father had founded and endowed the Stevens Institute of Technology in 1871. Wealthy as he was, he was even more widely known as a civil and mechanical engineer than for his family connections. Robert W. deForest was a New York lawyer and capitalist, and Daniel Runkle was a member of the family controlling the Warren Foundry, which was to supply the miles of pipe needed for the new project. Julian H. Kean was a member of the wealthy Elizabeth family prominent in utility, banking and public affairs in the State. Their prominence went back to the time of the Revolution, when their distinguished kinsman William Livingston was wartime Governor. There is reason to believe that Julian Kean, who was not overly interested in matters of business, held the directorship because his brother John Kean, Jr., was too busy with civic and other business affairs to attend Hackensack Water Company meetings regularly, and John, Jr., at times took Julian's place on the Board. In 1883 and in 1887, John was elected to

Congress, and in 1892 he was the Republican candidate for Governor of New Jersey in a campaign against a Democratic State machine which at the time had fallen into the hands of unabashed rascals. He lost by a few thousand votes.

Without question the most important action at the 1881 meeting was the election of Robert W. deForest as a director. For the next four decades, the Hackensack Water Company reflected the character of Robert W. deForest. We can only speculate what brought him into the group that took over the new enterprise; probably the fact that, as a son-in-law of the founder of the Central Railroad of New Jersey, he was one of the most important figures in the affairs of the railroad, with which the Stevens' and Kean's had close connections. Mr. de Forest was not a large stockholder at the outset, and may have originally been retained for his legal advice. It soon became clear that his business competence was of far more importance.

In a day when the anti-hero, the failure, is the popular figure, Robert W. deForest is something of an embarrassment, for he was so clearly admirable: to quote David Riesman's characterization of another such person, one of the ideal types of men who flourished in an era depending on inner-direction. Both the record and the recollections of men who knew him are at one: he was a leading member of the New York bar, a shrewd business man, a daring financier and the ablest philanthropist of his day. Robert deForest was born on Charles Street in New York, of a family so well established that it would have been an affront to call him socially prominent, and he had married a wealthy and intellectual descendant of another distinguished American family, Emily Johnston, whose father had founded the Central Railroad of New Jersey in defiance of the Camden and Amboy monopoly, and who herself was a person of great talent and distinction. The wide range of his activities staggers the imagination, and, what is more, his colleagues in each activity seem to have been persuaded that the particular one was his principal interest.

During the period when he was the President of the Hackensack Water Company, he was an officer and general counsel of the Central Railroad of New Jersey, head of an active Wall Street law firm, a leading figure in the Presbyterian Church in America, President of the Provident Loan Society (which he had helped to found as a philanthropic organization to drive down the exorbitant loan charges paid by the poor), President of the Charity Organization Society, New York's greatest private charitable organization, which he founded in order to merge the dozens of small duplicating charity efforts, an official of New York's Presbyterian Hospital, President of the Metropolitan Museum of Art and one of its principal benefactors (he and Mrs. deForest gave the American Wing of the Museum), and for a short time Commissioner of Tenements of the City of New York under Mayor Seth Low. He conceived, and prevailed upon Russell Sage to establish, what is said to be the first of the great foundations for charitable, research and educational purposes, the Russell Sage Foundation. Cheerful, modest and friendly, he was an excellent counterbalance to his austere and aloof brother Henry W. deForest, an equally able and successful lawyer and businessman who was his partner in the law firm of deForest Brothers. Despite the wide range of his activities, Robert deForest continued to lead the life of a very wealthy man, maintaining homes in New York City and on Long Island, in the Adirondacks and South Carolina. In short, like W. S. Gilbert's celebrated King, he wished all men as rich as he and he was rich as rich could be. Many years later, the *New York Times* hailed him on his eightieth birthday as New York's first citizen in philanthropy, whose eighty birthday candles "might easily stand for a separate branch of the civic and welfare work to which Robert Weeks deForest has devoted more than a half century of his life," and when he died on May 6, 1931, the tributes in the papers filled columns

Robert W. deForest, President 1885-1927
Courtesy Messrs. DeForest & Duer

of space, one of the most perceptive being that of Mayor James Walker, who said in the course of a brief eulogy in which he recounted Mr. deForest's contributions to the welfare of New York, "He was truly a New Yorker, one proud of his City and one in whom the City took as great a pride. Yet in all his work, so valuable to the people of this community and the nation, he remained in the background, modest and self-effacing."

The secret of his ability to do so many things was undoubtedly his phenomenal talent for finding and attracting competent men and for working with them. He made no pretense of having a brilliant mind; he was evidently slightly deaf and as Mayor Walker said, he seemed to make no effort to get his own way

J. & H. Van Buskirk Mill, c. 1880
Courtesy of Miss Helen Waite

in his charitable and business affairs. Things simply had a way of going as Mr. deForest thought best.

He was the very embodiment of the man of the late nineteenth and early twentieth centuries who had clear goals and righteously pursued them, of whom the best known public example was his friend Theodore Roosevelt (who was Commissioner of Police while he was Tenement Commissioner of New York); in fact, an even clearer example than Theodore Roosevelt of the inner-directed, self-assured man of the day, because he was never obliged by politics to concern himself about popular approval. At a time when it often seems more important to have good public relations than to provide good service or to make a good product, "where approval itself, irrespective of content, becomes almost the only unequivocal good," it is refreshing to go back in imagination to an age when there were men who were really convinced that their task was to live up to their own high standards, not to maintain good public relations.

When Mr. deForest and the other new men joined the Board of Directors of Hackensack Water Company, the new management began to push ahead with a vigor that astonished local people. By November 25, 1881, they had purchased eleven acres of land and the mill of J. & H. Van Buskirk, at New Milford,* for $50,000 in cash.

The mill-site was a very old one, a County history of 1882 says,

> "the first structure having been erected before the Revolutionary War and used at that period as a saw mill. It subsequently became a tannery and bleaching mill, after which it was devoted to the manufacture of buttons, and was later converted into a woolen mill. Jacob Van Buskirk [father of the current owners] in 1830 transformed it into a grist mill, and it is at the present time devoted to the manufacture of flour. It has three run of stone, and grinds rye and buckwheat extensively, together with feed."

---

* The site is in the present Borough of Oradell, which includes within its limits the old communities of Oradell and New Milford, not to be confused with the present Borough of New Milford. The Water Company's New Milford Plant takes its name from the original settlement, not the modern borough.

First Pumping Station and Circular Basin, c. 1885

J. & H. Van Buskirk also operated a large schooner, the "Kate Lawrence", 58 feet long, with a beam of 21 feet and having an almost life-sized female figure-head in the bow, to convey their produce down the river to New York and Paterson.

The new management ordered the necessary pumping engines and pipes and were making surveys to run the pipes along the Bergen Turnpike and to build a large reservoir at Weehawken, from which the water would flow by gravity down to Hoboken. By January, 1882, work had commenced on the transmission line.

It has always been an article of faith among older Water Company people that the reason why the line to Hoboken ran from New Milford to Hackensack along the railroad right-of-way was that a crowd of farmers armed with pitchforks stopped the digging along Kinderkamack Road, where the pipe was first intended to go. If so, their efforts to keep any public water supply from their doors succeeded for many years. The chances are that the Company itself regarded the railroad line, which ran close to the plant, as the cheapest and most direct route.

Fifty men were soon at work at New Milford, where "the walls of the building are being run up by a dozen bricklayers and concrete foundations laid for the building for the pumping engines." A chimney 135 feet high was under construction on a foundation nine feet thick, as well as a circular settling basin 110 feet in diameter in front of the building and a forty-eight inch circular brick conduit to a large pump well. These works appear to have cost $537,500. By spring, several divers and a vessel with a steam engine were busy at Ridgefield completing the river crossing there. Large gangs of workmen were living along the route, digging the trenches for the twenty-inch transmission line to the Weehawken low service reservoir. On July 26, 1882, Mr. D. W. Chase was hired as superintendent of the New Milford plant at $125 a month, house rent and fuel, and on November 1, 1882, Hackensack water began flowing to Hoboken. "The much talked about parade of the Fire Department in celebration of the event," the *Jersey City Argus* noted, "did not come off because the Tax Commissioners refused to appropriate the $400 that was asked to defray the expenses."

The Town of West Hoboken, which had previously had no public water supply, was not so penurious, and put on a fine parade:

> "The town in its infancy, like all country places, depended entirely on the various wells and cisterns for its drinking water, and . . . there were public pumps and cisterns in various parts of the town. In the spring of 1883, the Hackensack Water Company . . . began laying mains through Palisade Avenue, Clinton Avenue, Spring Street and Weav-

Weehawken Water Tower, c. 1885

ertown road. The water was turned on for domestic and
fire service on September 14, 1883, and this was an occasion
of great rejoicing by the citizens, a feature of which was a
grand parade, in which nearly every fire company in North
Hudson took part." *(Drescher, Wm. M., Jr., History of
West Hoboken, N.J.)*

On September 29, 1883, a new 15,000,000 gallon reservoir
and a water tower 175 feet high and thirty feet square was

placed on the line at Weehawken to maintain pressures at higher levels, the site being one of the highest points in the vicinity of Hoboken. The tank on the top floor of the water tower held 150,000 gallons and weighed 600 tons. Six stories tall, the building was a copy of the celebrated Palazzo Vecchio at Florence, and soon became a local landmark. The opening of the Weehawken office and the beginning of service at high levels was celebrated by a parade of the Fire Departments of Union Hill and West Hoboken, Engines Nos. 1 and 2 of Hoboken, Liberty Hose Co. of Hackensack, and others, including the Drum Corps.

The year 1883 marked a number of important milestones in Weehawken's history: the first train went through the newly-finished Weehawken tunnel and the ferryboat "Newburgh" began operating at the 42nd Street ferry, the first Roman Catholic Mass was celebrated and the first fire company was organized, the Baldwin Hose Company No. 1. The population was just over one thousand. Nearby in Union Hill stood the famous Peter Brewery, built in 1859, where Mr. Peter lived in a baronial Victorian mansion surrounded by painted lawn statues and elegant fountains, with his brewmasters ensconced in houses to the right and left. Union Hill was also the site of a considerable silk-weaving industry. The wealthy Simon family, like the Peters, lived a few doors from their plant, the Simon Silk Mill. To the east of the water tower, a large number of wealthy and prominent New Yorkers lived on the heights of the Palisades, where they could enjoy the view of the river and the City in bucolic surroundings a half hour from Times Square.

* * *

When the water tower was completed, the Company moved its Hoboken office to Weehawken, to centralize the general office and the high-level pumping operations. A horsecar line ran in front of the office to the Hoboken ferries.

Mr. William Shippen, the son of W. W. Shippen and secretary of the Company, made his headquarters there. The Shippens were a socially prominent family of New York and Hoboken, in a day when that was not said in jest, and lived in style at the latter place. Mrs. William Shippen was a particularly forceful woman, the acknowledged social arbiter of the fashionable resort of Sea Bright (which the W. W. Shippens had established at

Office in Weehawken Tower, c. 1885. The man at the right is
Charles E. Brush, the First Chief Engineer

about the time of the Civil War) and, Company gossips said, the acknowledged boss in the Shippen family, not at all hesitant to have her coachman drive her up to the Company office at Weehawken for the purpose of giving her husband her views on his current problems. She also insisted that one of the Company workmen come down to Hoboken and clean her cellar at intervals. On one such visit, the man from the Company, getting no answer at either the back door or the front door, and re-

High-level Pumping Equipment in Weehawken Tower, c. 1885

luctant to trudge back to Weehawken with the job undone, lifted a manhole cover in the sidewalk and slid down the coal-chute into the cellar. Mrs. Shippen, who had not heard him knocking but had no difficulty in hearing him land in the cellar, went down and sent him packing back to Weehawken with a stern lecture on breaking and entering houses. Mrs. Shippen thereafter used her own help for household cleaning.

*　　*　　*

Despite the fact that the new water system had a better source of supply than most public water suppliers in the New York area, and a far better source than the former station at Cherry Hill, the new owners ran into difficulties with water quality almost immediately. Some were doubtless caused by the new pipes, but many of the problems arose from a lack of knowledge about the treatment of organic growths in the water, which gave it a "fishy" taste, particularly at those times of year when algae multiplied rapidly in the reservoirs. Newspaper editors, who probably would cheerfully have admitted that they did not know enough about the water business to pour ditch water out of a boot, had a gala time over the Company's troubles. The *Hackensack Republican* carried the best story:

> "The reporter never drinks raw water, but the delicacy of his olfactory nerves enables him to assert boldly that his water has an ancient fish-like smell that is very offensive—one gentleman likens it unto the liquid that is used for freshening salt mackerel." *(February 5, 1885)*

At another time, when it had no smells to complain of, the *Republican* feared that the "water that comes through the pipes is so nearly the hue of milk that the two liquids will assimilate with much less danger of detection than ever before." When the algae season returned, it fell back on its "ancient fish-like smell" stories. Water engineers can see today that simple chemical treatment would have killed the organic matter, but at the time the poor officials of the Company could do nothing but curse their bad luck and the newspapers.

The *Democrat*, not to be outdone by the *Republican*, claimed in June, 1885, that it would soon be able to invite the directors of the Water Company to an eel dinner if the rate of catching them in its water motor continued. The Water Commissioners of Hoboken, while admitting that "there is hardly any city totally free from the trouble," made it plain that they believed that the sudden occurrence of quantities of eels implied "a suspicion as to the carefulness of those who furnish water to our city." They doubted (with some cause) the Water Company's explanation that the eels grew from spawn escaping into the mains through the screens, and openly speculated that the screening itself was defective. The *Democrat*, which had hitherto directed its jibes at the Company, now could not forebear aiming one at Hoboken:

> "The Hoboken people are kicking up a row over the Hackensack River water which they are given to drink. We wonder what they want. Do they expect the company to furnish them beer at the rates they pay for water?"

The Company seems in some way or other to have bested the eels, and manual cleaning of the reservoirs, along with a plan devised by Professor Leeds of Stevens Institute for forcing compressed air into the water at New Milford, seems to have helped the odors. The compressed air, a Hudson County publication reported, entirely restored the water's vitality. "The trouble immediately ceased and the water has since been of exceptional purity." In all candor, this was over-optimistic, for the algae problem was not really solved for years. The complaints were good-natured enough and doubtless were so understood by readers, whatever the Water Company people thought. Even the *Republican*, in a more sober mood, was frank to say:

> "When we hear of neighboring towns like Passaic with 30 or 40 cases of typhoid fever attributed to impure water supply, contaminated wells and defective drainage, we should be heartily grateful that we have an abundant supply of pure water from the Hackensack Water Works . . ." *(January 31, 1889.)*

The equally caustic *Democrat* confessed at least once that "the management of the company has been in every way satisfactory to its ever-increasing list of consumers and to the towns and cities it supplies with water . . ." and at another time (when it was engaged in civic promotion, to be sure) it was almost ecstatic about Hackensack's water supply:

75

"The river receives constant supplies from the overflow of Rockland Lake; we are, therefore, provided with a bountiful supply of pure cold water that is constantly appreciated and enjoyed by our citizens. To that unusually excellent supply of water for domestic uses, may be attributed much of the healthfulness that is enhancing the reputation of this town as a place for permanent residence." *(Bergen County Democrat's History of Hackensack, N. J. p. 73.)*

There were times in the next few years when Company people must have wondered whether the *Bergen County Democrat* and the *Bergen Evening Record* were writing about the same river.

The new owners of the Hackensack Water Company had entered the water business at a most fortunate time, whether by luck or foresight it is hard to say. If their original plan had been to serve only Hoboken and Hackensack and the people along the route of their transmission lines it was luck, because so far as Hoboken was concerned, it soon became clear that the Company's estimates of the quantity of water needed for the 30,000 residents were grossly in error. Unfortunately, the City of Hoboken, not the Company, owned the distribution system, and the per capita usage turned out to be more than twice as high as normal. Water Company people suspected with cause that it was not because the local people were addicted to bathing or indeed to using water as a drink, but because about 65% was lost through leakage and simple waste. The City's system leaked like a sieve. Repeated surveys showed that faucets were allowed to run wide open in cold weather to keep pipes from freezing and sometimes out of sheer malice. The Company was often forced to pay Jersey City $300 a day for water to supplement its supply, a payment which exceeded the amount received from Hoboken for the day. Repeated complaints to the Water Commissioners of Hoboken about the maintenance of their pipes went unanswered. The few meters that were installed brought nothing but ill will when people found themselves and not the Water Company paying for their waste. If Hoboken had been the Company's only source of revenue over the years, it would have been engaged in a poor business indeed. What Hoboken did provide was the incentive to enter the water business, and revenue enough to keep the business going (prob-

Debarking from Commuting Train at Englewood, c. 1883
Englewood Public Library

ably with no concern for depreciation and little concern for a return on the stockholders' investment) until Bergen County and the north Hudson towns were built up enough to pay their way as water customers.

Englewood, for example, was a prosperous commuting town a few miles northeast of Hackensack.

"Attractively situated in the most desirable portion of Bergen County [one observer wrote], the bright and growing village of Englewood is rapidly advancing to the front as one of the most prosperous in this section of the State. . . . [Many business men of the metropolis, he went on, have erected] handsome residences, surrounded with grounds tastily designed and cultivated. . . . The streets, while not paved, are nearly always in first-class condition, and form excellent driveways, which, during the warmer months, resound with the pattering hoofs of the speedy roadsters, behind which are seated the wealth and beauty of the village."

By 1885 it had outgrown its wells and cisterns and was looking for a public water supply. The town, in fact, was torn by a controversy on the subject, aired at great length in the *Englewood Times*. Some people favored artesian wells, other leading citizens proposed a plan for drawing water from the Long Swamp Brook near Madison Avenue in Schraalenburgh, some favored a municipal supply, and still others a private local water company.

In July, 1886, the Hackensack Water Company, which was about to lay a second transmission main from its plant in New Milford to Hoboken, was able to add Englewood to the system by making a deviation in the line so as to take in the village. "The Company," the *Englewood Times* said, "is very strong financially, they have established moderate rates, and the character of the water is excellent. It is a matter of congratulation that the prospect is so bright for having a water supply." The new line was in operation by the end of September, 1887.

Oradell, next to the pumping station, was another example of the growing need for water in Bergen County. In September, 1887, a number of capitalists and local businessmen, including

Map of Hackensack and Vicinity. *1876 Bergen County Atlas*

Henry Bellis and C. Blauvelt of Oradell (both of whom were long associated with the Company) and Jacob Van Buskirk of New Milford (the prior owner of the pumping station site), formed the Oradell Land Improvement Co. to take advantage of the new interest in suburban homes. Before the Hackensack Water Company laid pipes in the streets, a bathtub was some-

79

thing of a novelty in Oradell. Edward Demarest recalls that his father was the fortunate possessor of the first bathtub in town.

"The old house at 357 Maple Avenue where Demarest was born claimed the first bathtub in Oradell. Demarest's uncle, a plumber, had made a zinc bathtub for some rich people in Westwood. He told Demarest's father, 'Charlie, there's no reason why you shouldn't have a bathtub, too.'

"Charlie Demarest, always anxious to try something new, became the owner of a wood-paneled zinc-lined bathtub. Demarest says the water had to be pumped into a huge zinc storage tub in the attic which connected to the bathtub directly below it in the bathroom." (The *Record*, February 10, 1969.)

Towns like River Edge, Ridgefield Park, Ridgefield, Fairview, West New York and Union Hill, along the lines of the first transmission main, and Dumont, Bergenfield, Tenafly and Leonia, along later lines, became part of the system as a matter of course. Teaneck, Closter, Westwood, and others near the lines were attached when enough customers expressed interest to justify the cost of extending the lines. Plans to extend to Rutherford were held up temporarily by litigation and by political conflicts within the town government. J. P. Cooper, the mayor and owner of a local lumber yard, who was said to be "a man of progressive ideas and wide experience" and a leader in modernizing the town, opposed the franchise. "Possessed [of] a striking personality and great vigor of mind, . . . and an acute reasoner and ready debater," like many such men he delighted in controversy, and the Water Company issue may well have been little more than a new opportunity to put himself at variance with the Council, who favored the franchise. In any event the ordinance was quickly passed over his veto, and before long Rutherford and the towns immediately to the north were also added to the system.

It is easy enough to write, in this centennial year of 1969, about adding this town or that to the system. In a day of traction ditchers and huge earthmoving equipment, it is hard to remember that each shovelful of dirt in each foot of main was lifted from trenches six feet deep or more by workmen with long-handled shovels, who often stood knee-deep in water to do the digging, that each length of pipe was let down into the trench on ropes by hand and connected by hand and that each trench

Digging Trench in Palisade Avenue, Englewood, for First Water Line 1887. (Note Bystander with Bicycle) *Englewood Public Library*

was back-filled with the same shovels that dug them. Much of the water that the people of Bergen and Hudson Counties drink today is the product of the back-breaking labor of hundreds of men now dead, many of them Italian, who came to America and toiled so that their children and their children's children would have a better life than their fathers had. Many of these men never worked anywhere else, and were in the employ of the Company until the day they retired, a day, fortunately, when they drove machines, instead of driving themselves. The Hackensack Water Company has always been proud of them, and flatters itself that they were proud of the Company.

1890-1902

The deForests, the Stevens' and the Keans had both the means and daring to take risks involved in building a water system well beyond the immediate needs of the territory and well beyond the immediate prospects of a fair return on their investment, in the confidence that later growth would make the capital expenditure worth while. The distribution system they built was the backbone of the system which served the people of northeastern New Jersey for many years, though now almost completely superseded by modern lines.

The problems that the early builders faced were not merely problems of risking capital, as their experience in Englewood was soon to show. They had cheerfully diverted a transmission line and put in a distribution system there, evidently without reflecting that the area east of the railroad rose out of the valley so rapidly that many of the finest houses in the village, east of Lydecker Street, would have very little pressure and at times possibly none at all. The matter was brought forcibly to the attention of the Company and local people in September, 1890, when a disgruntled servant set fire to a house in that area while the family were summering in the Adirondacks. Englewood's firemen were on the scene almost at once, but did little more than watch the house burn, for their hoses were unable to throw a stream to the second floor. The *Press* observed sharply that "the hydrants are ornamental, and make excellent tie posts for horses, but for practical fire purposes are of no account." The local press, and doubtless some of the people at the higher elevations, were half convinced that the Company had deliberately defrauded them in failing to provide pressure. What they did not know, and to tell the truth the Company made little effort to explain, was that the matter was not a case of negligence or indifference, but a complicated engineering problem. After a delay that would have appalled a public relations expert, the Company finally let the residents know that they too were concerned. "Mr. Charles E. Brush, the engineer of the Hackensack Water Company, accompanied by Mr. Myles Tierney, the engineer of the [Harlem River] Washington Bridge and also one of the Directors of the Water Company . . ," the *Englewood Times* reported at the end of March, 1891, "went carefully over the ground with a view of ascertaining the best means of giving the town a high pressure water service."

Actually, so far as the Water Company was concerned, the idea of serving the higher levels of the Palisades was very appealing. The area promised to grow rapidly, with a new bridge planned over the Hudson at 59th Street, and with a new railroad along the ridge of the Palisades even more imminent after being in planning stages for nearly twenty years. (Neither the bridge nor the railroad, of course, was ever built.)

The difficulty was that the hydraulic problems involved in serving both the lower portions of Englewood, only a few feet above sea level, and the three hundred foot heights of the Palisades were not fully solved. At the very least, an expensive additional pumping station would be needed for the purpose. If the Palisades Railroad was completed the water demand promised to rise sharply, so much so that Mr. Brush's report suggested that the high service be made adequate to serve Alpine, several miles to the north, and a large capital outlay would be necessary for any solution. "Until recently," Mr. Brush wrote concerning the possibility of reaching levels up to

four and five hundred feet above the mains, "that has seemed
to be impracticable, but the later accomplishments in hydraulic
engineering was demonstrated that it is possible. . . ." Englewood, of course, was little interested in other people's engineering problems, and was sharply critical of the Company for not
going ahead immediately.

Elevated Tank
at Englewood
c. 1890

However embarrassed the Company officials were to discover that they had laid pipes in an area that could not be
served with the existing pressures, they gave no public hint of
it. In their own good time they built an advanced type of high-

pressure pumping station at Demarest Avenue, near the railroad tracks, at great expense, with every facility duplicated to assure continuous service—two 2,000,000 gallon per day pumps and two independent steam engine systems. Water was taken through a twelve inch line from the 24 inch transmission main in Palisade Avenue. The magnitude of the work involved was impressive indeed to local people, who had heretofore been grumbling at the penury of a Company that (so far as they could see) simply refused to run its pumps a little faster to raise pressures for its customers. Even the local newspaper, which had been leading the attack, became almost effusive about the thorough and workmanlike manner in which the work was being done "under the personal supervision of Mr. Myles Tierney, who is one of the most competent engineers in this line of work in the United States."

"The size and expense of the plant," the newspaper said, "shows conclusively that the Hackensack Water Company has faith in the future growth and prosperity of Englewood." The Company also got a little additional free publicity out of the Demarest Avenue pumping station in April 1893, when, as the *Press* reported it,

> "A team of horses belonging to the Hackensack Water Company, while feeding near the railroad Tuesday noon, took fright as Conductor Graham's train came down and made a break for liberty. One went north and was soon caught. The other started south, ahead of the train and down the track, making splendid time until the culvert near Nordhoff was reached. This the horse tried to jump, and so much of it as did not clear by the leap, he made on a slide that would have done any baseball enthusiast good to see. For a moment the horse lay quiet at the further end of the culvert, then got on his feet again and ran as far as Nordhoff where it turned into the Phelps' property and re-

86

ceived a fall into a ditch. Here it was captured, and, what is most wonderful about the episode, was found not to be seriously injured. Conductor Graham says he would like to buy that horse as one that can beat his train from Englewood to Nordhoff is worth owning." *(Englewood Press, April 22, 1893.)*

Eight or ten years later the whole business of pressures had been forgotten. When J. A. Humphrey, one of Englewood's first commuters, came to write its history in 1899, his observations probably reflected the views of most Englewood people:

"The supply has always been abundant and satisfactory, and it is very fortunate for this town that the Hackensack Water Company finds it convenient to pass our doors. This will be appreciated more by those who for years were compelled to pump their water from wells and cisterns that often ran dry than by those that never experienced that labor."

Mr. Humphrey remembered all too well that when Englewood's wells ran dry, people were compelled to buy water at one dollar for each load, and, though he was too decorous to say so, undoubtedly also remembered that in the days before the water lines came to town many Englewood people washed with pitchers and basins in their bedrooms and used the privies behind their houses. The day was soon to come when no one remembered the labor of pumping water from wells, the pitchers and basins or the privies, and few indeed, if they thought about the matter at all, felt any gratitude whatever for a public water supply.

The short-lived Panic of 1893 had little effect on the Company's expansion. At the bottom of the depression, in December, 1893, the Directors resolved "that this Company, instead of stopping work on its new Reservoir [at Weehawken] during the winter months, as has heretofore been its intention, direct the contractor to continue to employ a full force of men . . . in the belief that the best remedy for the threatened distress among the laboring classes is for private employers to give out work whenever possible." It takes little imagination to see the

Architect's Drawing of First New Milford Pumping Station
Charles E. Brush, 1881

hand of Robert W. deForest in this, for, as we have seen, he was deeply concerned about the problems of working-men in a day when all too few business men were prepared to let public welfare affect their business decisions. By 1895, business was booming again. At about this time, electric lights supplanted the gas lights along Main Street in Hackensack.

On June 4, 1897, the Company lost Mr. Charles E. Brush, its distinguished Chief Engineer, who died at his home in New York City. He was 55 years old, a college professor, the engineer of three water companies and a street railway company, and a consulting engineer of the New York and New Jersey Bridge Company, the man who laid out the system which continues seventy years later to be the framework of the water distribution network in most of Bergen County and northern Hudson County, a great pioneer in the field of water engineering. Mr. Brush was one example, of which there were many, of Robert W. deForest's ability to seek out and attract the leading men in their fields for his enterprises. The beautiful small Victorian building which still stands at the south end of the New Milford plant is at least one monument to Mr. Brush's skill as an architect.

Myles Tierney, who was also attracted by Mr. deForest, was a man of totally different background, of wide-ranging interests of his own, and was as important to the Company in engineering and construction as Mr. deForest was in administration and finance. Except for his size, Myles Tierney "looked the image of General Grant." Six foot three inches tall and weighing over two hundred pounds, with a red spade-beard, he had been born on a farm in Silver Lake, Pennsylvania, of Irish immigrant parents. His schooling consisted of a few years in a log school in the back country of Pennsylvania. He came to Jersey City early in life, went into the contracting business, and soon rose to eminence in the field. He built many apartment houses in Jersey City and Hoboken, built a part of the Sixth Avenue Elevated in New York City, and built the Washington Bridge over the Harlem River. He never lost the reserved ways of his early farm life, and his great dignity and distinguished appearance are still remembered by everyone who knew him.

He became President of the Hudson Trust Company in Hoboken, a bank having close connections with Andrew Carnegie and with many large monied interests in New York. During his lifetime Colonel Stevens, who owned a large part of the City of Hoboken, frequently consulted with him about business affairs. He was a Trustee of St. Patrick's Cathedral, a Knight of St. Gregory, and a leader in every charitable endeavor of his church. He was held in such high esteem by the de Forests, Keans, and Stevens', who controlled the Water Company, that

Myles Tierney
Courtesy Hudson Trust Company

he was named a Vice President, and called in as an outside contractor to handle every construction job that the Company undertook, "on the usual basis" that is, at his cost, whatever it might turn out to be, plus a contractor's fee.

In a day when the de Forests, Stevens' and Keans were spending their own money for Mr. Tierney's work, there is little doubt that the Company got its money's worth and more from every job he did. As might be expected, however, many employees of the Company, who worked for the few dollars a day that people were paid in those times, grumbled about "Ten Per Cent Tierney", who was getting richer and richer from his contracting and banking, while they had all they could do to pay their daily expenses. At the turn of the century, as in earlier years, there was a great gulf between the well-to-do and the ordinary workingman; indeed, the greatest contrast between American life in 1890 and life a half century later may well lie in the distance then and now between the rich and poor, in income, manner of living and status in the community. It is easy to understand—particularly since Mr. Tierney seldom made any effort to hide his blunt, gruff ways in dealing with subordinates—the glee with which Company people told (probably with gross exaggeration) of one of his run-ins with Bill Smith. Smith had come to the New Milford plant to install some pumps for the Worthington Company and never left. At the time he was in charge of pumping operations at New Milford.

Vice President Tierney came in one day while directing work on the reservoir and tried to lecture Smith for some supposed dereliction. Smith, who had frequently been admonished by Superintendent D. W. French about his profane language (in writing, not in person—there were limits to French's own courage), gave one of his best expositions of that art, picked up a huge wrench and started after Tierney shouting "If you don't get out of here I'll break you in two." Vice President Tierney got out and Mr. Smith continued to work happily for the Company until the day of his death, a quarter of a century later.

Bill Smith not only had a low opinion of Vice Presidents; like most self-trained men he had little use for people who had gotten their knowledge from books. Many years later, when a newly hired engineering college graduate came running in to Smith's office one day to report that one of the steam engines had failed, Smith told him to go fix it himself, and when he asked "What am I going to fix it with?" Smith pointed to a sledge-hammer and chisel standing in the corner of the office. After his visitor had shown a proper amount of shock and amazement at this nonsense, Smith took up the two tools and went out and started the engine, by what means only Bill Smith knew.

*   *   *

The expansion of the Water Company was only one of dozens of evidences of the growth of the area in those days.

Trolley Cars at Edgewater Ferry Terminal, c. 1908
North Jersey Chapter,
National Railway Historical Society, Inc. Collection

Trolley lines, a contemporary observer wrote, "are fast changing not only the old mode of travel, but are also opening up new fields for country homes which steam car lines fail to reach." A horse car line from Hoboken had run along Park Avenue in Weehawken since the 1860's, operated by the Hoboken & Weehawken Horse Car Company, of which Mr. John H. Bonn was President. Mr. Bonn, who had also been a director of the Hackensack Water Company for several years and may well have suggested the Weehawken tower site, was a most inventive and energetic man. In 1874 he conceived and built a steam elevator at Hoboken to lift passenger-laden street cars, with the horses attached, to the top of the bluff at West Hoboken. He also built an elevated cable railroad from Hoboken to Jersey City Heights. On October 23, 1891, he completed a second elevator on the Palisades east of the Water Company office at Weehawken, which carried street cars down to the ferries, two hundred feet below. He died soon after, but not until he had initiated the work of electrifying the horse car lines in the area. The introduction of electric motive power made it possible for street cars to run far beyond the city limits, and on March 6, 1896, the Bergen County Traction Company was formed to build a line from the Edgewater Ferry up the steep incline to the top of the Palisades, and north and west to Englewood. (Its original line was extended to Tenafly in 1907.) The line started operation on July 11, 1896, with four open cars and six closed ones. Service began on its branch line to Hackensack on February 24, 1899, with a gala trolley ride and dinner for local officials. The *Bergen Evening Record* greeted the first cars with the headline "Bells clang through town today and will do so from now on to eternity." By 1903, trolleys ran from Hoboken to Hackensack over the old Bergen Turnpike, and thence north to Fairmount, and before long the Hudson River Line was extended through Maywood and Arcola to Paterson, and another line was built through Lodi, Garfield, Hasbrouck Heights, Wood Ridge, Rutherford and south to Newark. Still other trolley lines came directly into Rutherford from the east, and an interurban electric railroad ran from Paterson through Ridgewood as far north as Suffern. Fifty years ago, one of the great pleasures of a trip to Hackensack in the summer was a ride in the spacious open Hudson River street cars, with the added excitement of the conductor sidling along the long outside step to reach in and collect the nickel fare, the motorman up front, with one hand on the upright throttle, the other on the brake control and his foot on the

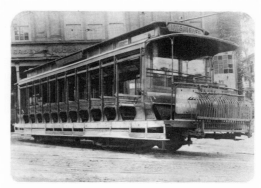

Open Trolley Car, Hudson River Line, c. 1915
North Jersey Chapter
National Railway Historical Society, Inc. Collection

gong. Each new line opened more territory for suburban development and each new development needed water.

The year 1899, which saw the first street car lines in Hackensack, also marked the establishment of the Hackensack Trust Company and the Hackensack Golf Club, whose spacious clubhouse on Summit Avenue joined the older Oritani Field Club on Main Street as a social center for the well-to-do.

* * *

Great advances in the field of public water supply were made in the last years of the nineteenth century. Microscopic studies of water were beginning to isolate the algae and other organisms

94

that caused the tastes and odors which plagued the water suppliers, and to give some promise of ending that annoyance.

American waterworks engineers had also been doing some experimentation in the use of filters. Originally conceived only as a means of reducing turbidity, clearing the color and taking out the organic materials which caused odors, recent studies had shown filtration to be even more useful in reducing the number of harmful bacteria in water, often with dramatic results in areas where there had been a high incidence of water-borne disease before filtration. Real research in America did not begin until about 1887, when Allen Hazen built and operated an experimental filter at the Lawrence Experiment Station in Massachusetts.

Sand filters had been in use for many years in some of the more advanced countries of Europe, in places where the dense population had contaminated the watersheds. One hundred twenty filters, each having an area of one acre, were in use in London, and Berlin had 22 filters of two acres each. In 1899 it was estimated that filtered water was supplied to about 11,000,000 people in England, 4,600,000 in Germany, 1,400,000 in Holland and perhaps 3,000,000 in the rest of Europe. A few similar filters had been built in the United States, only two of which served systems of a size comparable to the Hackensack system: Poughkeepsie, New York, built in 1872, and Albany, New York built in 1899. In America, less than a half million people were supplied with water from these slow sand filters. Scattered throughout the country, there were also a number of "patent" filters, so-called "tub filters" or "mechanical filters", including one or two systems built in the last few years before 1899 with a nominal capacity equal to the demands on the Hackensack system. They served, in fact, a larger aggregate number of Americans than the European-type filter systems, but they were really designed for industrial plants, rather than public water supplies. The salient fact, however, was that except in the south and west, where muddy river waters had to be cleared, very few

Oradell Station c. 1905
Oradell Free Public Library

water supplies were being filtered at the turn of the century. To this day the New York City, Jersey City, Wanaque Reservoir and Newark supplies (to mention only four out of hundreds) are not filtered.

On October 26, 1899, doubtless feeling with some justification that it was in the forefront of progress, the Hackensack Water Company hired Mr. Hazen to see "what results could be accomplished by the different methods of filtration." He was the leading proponent of the so-called "slow sand filters", in which the water was allowed to percolate slowly down through a huge bed of sand, perhaps at a rate of 1½ or 2 million gallons a day (MGD) per acre. At Louisville, another engineer, George W. Fuller, was experimenting with a rapid sand filter, in which the rate of flow was expected to be increased fifty-fold or more by pretreatment of the water with coagulants. The Fuller system seemed to have many attractions, but it was controversial and virtually untried in large plants. The system was based on the principle of the patented

Veldran Mill, c. 1895

"tub filters", the patents on which had recently expired, but the Louisville plant, if built, would be the first to use large concrete filters suitable for a supply like that of the Hackensack Water Company. We do not know what Mr. Hazen reported, probably that if the Company decided to filter its supply it should build a ten or fifteen acre slow sand system, but he undoubtedly pointed out that since the Hackensack River carried a good deal of organic material, the first step in any filter system would have to be the construction of at least a small reservoir in which the river water could settle out suspended matter.

Meanwhile, the Company determined to go ahead with a new reservoir at Oradell. It bought the old E. P. Veldran mill, a half mile or so north of the New Milford plant, and, if the report in the papers on December 18, 1901, was correct, paid $1,000,000 for large amounts of additional land north of the mill. The mill-site, which had been used for more than a century, was located at a point where an island divided the Hackensack River into two channels, and two dams created the head of water that drove the mill wheel. (The famous "triple dam", at the same spot, was created some years later when floods cut a third channel through the island, which was then filled with sheet piling and stone.) Veldran operated the mill "on a large scale, . . . buying his grain by the carload from the West."

The Company started at once to chop down the trees and pull up the stumps in a large area above the Beaverdam, a slough which ran off the Hackensack River above the celebrated Picnic Grove, which lay just north of modern Grove Street, in Oradell.

Triple Dam at Veldran Mill, c. 1905
Oradell Free Public Library

The New York engineering and construction firm of Mack & Moeller were hired to handle the job. The work had hardly begun before all of northern New Jersey was inundated by a great flood, which nearly caused a disaster:

> "Woodchoppers at work clearing the newly acquired tract of the Hackensack Water Company near Beaver Dam were obliged to chain the logs together and fasten them

Tract Being Cleared for First Oradell Reservoir, 1902
Courtesy Mr. Melvin E. King
(Mr. King is the larger of the two boys in the picture)

securely to prevent the timber from drifting away with the tide.

"The flood in the Hackensack Valley has now somewhat subsided and the people rested easier last night. A *Record* representative visited the flooded district yesterday afternoon and saw a vast sea of water almost washing the railroad tracks at Cherry Hill and stretching eastward as far as the eye could reach and northward to Oradell entirely cutting off travel at New Milford.

"At the latter place the road from the railroad depot to the Hackensack Water Company's plant was completely submerged, the water rushing over it in a torrent and cutting it full of holes. A man, handicapped with a bundle, attempted to wade across this road to the station. The water kept getting deeper until it looked like it was going to be a swimming match, when he was warned back.

Peter Cosney, a river fisherman, ferried the man over in a rowboat. Peter was kept busy carrying passengers." *(Bergen Evening Record, March 3, 1902.)*

1902 Flood at New Milford Plant
Residence of Superintendent D. W. Chase at left

Within a month the work was under way again and by April, 1902, the *Record* reported that

> "A stump-pulling machine, operated by steam, is at work clearing the new tract at Oradell. An electric dynamo will run the dredge in excavating for the large lake which it is proposed to build in what was until recently a dense growth of timber and underbrush, a veritable wilderness." *(Bergen Evening Record, April 2, 1902.)*

An "orange-peel" steam shovel, with a boom perhaps 75 feet long, was sent into the cleared area and dug a small lake, perhaps one hundred fifty to two hundred feet wide and a half-mile long. A suction dredge with two small six-inch pumps was then put into the lake to widen and deepen it, with only moderate success, but a reservoir holding about 250,000,000 gallons of water was the result.

The two old dams, the "Stony Dam" to the east and the Veldran Dam to the west, were not materially changed, and Mr. Veldran continued to operate his mill under a dollar-a-year lease for almost ten years. (Before the construction of the small reservoir both the Veldran Mill and the Collignon Mill at River-vale caused the Water Company a great deal of trouble in dry spells by holding back the whole flow of the stream so that their mills could be operated on half-day shifts. Mr. Melvin King, of Oradell, particularly remembers the friction between Mr. D. W. Chase of the Water Company and the Collignons over their practice of dumping sawdust in the mill-race to hold back water during droughts. The Water Company finally bought the Collignon property.)

Dredging First Oradell Reservoir, 1902
Courtesy Mr. Melvin E. King

Rocking Chair Ferry over Hackensack River after 1903 Flood
Courtesy Mr. Melvin E. King

Along with the reservoir, the Company authorized an enlargement of the pumping station at New Milford, with a new
110 foot chimney, new steam boilers giving the plant a capacity
of 1000 horsepower, and a pumping capacity of 12,000,000
gallons a day. The old Van Buskirk mill, built in 1873 on the
site of a pre-Revolutionary mill, had been torn down in 1899
to make room for the enlarged plant.

The reservoir would perform two functions. First, of course,
it would store water against periods of drought. Second, it was
expected that by giving the water time to settle, it would eliminate much of the sediment which the stream picked up in its

course through the low wooded and marshy land which ran for some miles north of Oradell. The New England filtered supplies depended heavily on large reservoirs back of the filter beds. The Company may or may not have known that the storage would eliminate a good part of any harmful bacteria that found their way into the stream, since most such bacteria have a short life span in clear water. If, as seems to have been the case, the work on the new reservoir in the spring of 1902 produced the discolored water that started a flood of complaints about the water supply and its purity, there may have been those in the plant at New Milford who wished the Company had let the poor bacteria live.

Weehawken General Office of Company, c. 1895
The Structure Still Exists as Part of the
Present Weehawken Office Building

In authorizing the reservoir and enlarged pumping station, the Company took no action to authorize a filter plant. Perhaps it was merely taking one step at a time, since a reservoir was required before any filter system could have been built. More probably the officers considered that the recent experiments in the art of rapid sand filtration made it wise to wait and see whether Mr. Hazen's slow sand filters or the new

"American" rapid sand filters of George W. Fuller were better.

They would have been sure that anyone was out of his mind who suggested that if they did not proceed at once they would be blackguarded for rascals and narrowly escape indictment. No large filter plant had ever been built in New Jersey and very few had been built in the whole country, and there was no reason to suppose that the Company could not move with reasonable prudence and still be far ahead of other water companies.

They were soon to be disabused. They had arrived in the modern world of newspaper headlines, where good men were easily filled with righteous but misdirected anger and the public was quick to believe that it was being imposed upon. All that was necessary to start an avalanche of trouble was a single mistake that made a dramatic newspaper story.

Water purity, which had pretty much been taken for granted in the past—particularly in the Hackensack territory, which had been free of typhoid while other areas in the east suffered devastating epidemics—had recently come very much to the public mind, partly because there had been a good deal of recent scientific study of water pollution, and partly because there had been several well-publicized studies showing a low incidence of typhoid in those Central European cities where the water was filtered as compared with American cities, where it usually was not. The medical journals undoubtedly spread the same word among physicians. (Chlorination, which is very effective against bacteria, and now in almost universal use, was not introduced in America until 1908, when the Jersey City supply was so treated. The Hackensack water began to be chlorinated soon afterwards.)

*   *   *

In 1895, a new publisher had come to Hackensack and started a new daily paper, *The Evening Record and Bergen*

County Herald. Shortly after its establishment, it was taken over by James A. Romeyn, a young gentleman descended from a long line of ministers of the Hackensack Dutch Reformed Church, who had recently graduated from Rutgers College and Columbia Law School. He had found the practice of law distasteful after a short try at it, and had a mother wealthy enough to indulge his tastes. He evidently found his relaxed attitude equally unsuitable for newspaper publishing, for in September 1901, almost two decades before the present management of the *Record* took over, the paper passed into the hands of Caleb Whitcomb of Rochester, New York.

Steam Elevator at Weehawken
which Lowered Passenger-laden Trolleys
and Other Vehicles to 42nd Street Ferry at Foot of Palisades, c. 1895

James A. Romeyn had prided himself on his moderation; the new owner seemed to feel that a new policy was indicated.

Where the old *Democrat* and the old *Republican* had been content to ridicule the Water Company for its "fishy" water in the algae season, and occasionally to indulge in a little dignified abuse of its management for not furnishing crystal-clear spring water, or for failing to backfill a road opening properly, the *Record*, under Whitcomb, took the tack that the fishy odor was merely the outward evidence of a broth of death-dealing germs.

It was, of course, the heyday of the sensational journalism of Pulitzer and Hearst and of the "muckrakers," a term Theodore Roosevelt borrowed from Bunyan's description of the man in *Pilgrim's Progress* who "looked no way but downward," and even when offered a crown "continued to rake to himself the filth of the floor." It was a comforting name to those who were pilloried (principally politicians and business men), but it may not have been entirely fair. The muckrakers brought about many reforms that were long overdue, for example the Pure Food and Drug Act, regulation of life insurance companies, public utility regulation, truth-in-advertising laws and many railroad safety laws.

In some ways the most revealing aspect of muckraking was not the truth or falsity of the allegations (in fact, as one former muckraker himself said, men were often "tried and found guilty in magazine counting-rooms before the investigation was begun"), but that the writers were saying what large numbers of people wanted to hear, and that in a nation brought up on Horatio Alger and commonly thought to worship enterprise, there were large numbers of men who were prepared to turn savagely on those who practised it. Self-satisfied business men would have been wise to consider the causes of public distrust, and to mend their ways, and some of them did. People being what they are, it is not surprising that many others preferred instead to mend their public images. "The muckrakers used publicity as an anti-business weapon," one historian has said, "and industry, in direct reply . . . , [saw] that if publicity could be used against them, it could also be used for them. Hence the birth of the whole public relations industry." Whether this was a boon or not may be left to wiser heads. The Water Company for its part chose neither to change its plans nor to begin a public-relations campaign, but to rely on its perhaps over-developed consciousness of rectitude, and to go on about its business. It might have been wiser to have been a little less self-assured.

It is not entirely clear how much the *Record* had to do with building up the unsafe water story at the outset. The paper's reports were calculated, and perhaps correctly, to give the impression that the County Medical Association had been the first mover. The only evidence to the contrary is that the other newspapers of the county treated the whole affair as a circulation-building scheme, not as a medical association project. There can be no doubt that the *Record* and the medical association, having first convinced themselves of the righteousness of the cause in which they saw themselves engaged, each played its own part very skillfully in convincing the public that the water was unsafe and that the Water Company officials were callous men concerned only with the quantity of water they could sell and not at all with its quality.

The newspaper's motives were probably unimpeachable, but whether they were or not the fact was that the Water Company gave it a clear opening for the attacks by failing to maintain one of its elevated water tanks with proper care, and this failure brought the whole system into question. In the early summer of 1902, at the height of the algae season and during the construction of the first Oradell reservoir, the water distributed to Rutherford, East Rutherford and Carlstadt became particularly "fishy." The source of the trouble seemed to be the Carlstadt tank, from which the three towns were served. When the tank was examined by local authorities, the top surface was covered with a most unappetizing green slime of algae which, however germ-free, should have been cleaned off long before. Eels, which also probably added little to the quality of drinking water, particularly dead eels, were to be seen in the tank. That was bad enough, but as luck would have it, a neighborhood cat had recently climbed the tower and fallen into the tank, with even more disastrous results. The reporters understandably made the most of their find, and there was nothing whatever that the Water Company could say to excuse the deplorable condition of the tank. The Company was in fact grievously at fault.

Aroused by their findings at the Carlstadt tank, the Boards of Health of the three towns and the officers of the county medical association set out to prove that the whole source of supply was polluted. The physician of the Rutherford Board of Health, accompanied by another doctor from the medical association, both men well regarded as physicians, went through the watershed looking for sources of pollution, and of course found them. At Oradell, they reported, "several houses of the poorer classes have behind them chicken yards by the side of a steep bank." There were dairy farms on the slopes along the Dwarskill, several miles to the north, and a pig pen was found on a small sluggish brook leading into the Dwarskill, miles above the intake. Here and there they found outhouses near streams in the watershed. At Demarest, on the Tenakill, the local pond was covered with algae, which was catalogued along with the outhouses, as was the fact that the drainage from the public roads ran into the river. None of these probably resulted in pollution at the outlet of the reservoir, but they made unpleasant reading.

The doctors who made the inspection did not say, if they knew, that they could have found the same conditions or worse in nearly every watershed serving New York and the surrounding country.

At the same time that the report was released, the Company received an even worse blow. Dr. St. John, the highly-respected head of the county medical association, announced that he had received a report from a bacteriologist, to whom he sent a sample of the water, that it was unfit for drinking purposes, and he, in turn, recommended that all water be boiled before use. The Water Company was shrewd enough not to argue with the head of the county medical association, but if it was not an isolated case of high bacteria count, there was a good chance that the count was due as much to delay in testing as to the quality of the sample. Water Company officials were able to say only that the report was at variance with every report the Water Company had ever received on the subject.

Main Street Hackensack, c. 1905
Post Card Collection of Mr. Gerry de la Ree

Superintendent French did his best to quiet the storm that followed. He denied that the Company was indifferent to the quality of its water, pointing out that the Company maintained a regular inspector of the watershed and made every effort to suppress nuisances, and asked for the aid of the medical association or anyone else in correcting them. He pointed out also that there were upwards of two hundred streams in the watershed, which was considered one of the cleanest in the state, and that in view of its immense area, it was remarkable that so few instances of improper conditions could be found. He insisted that the report that the water was unfit for use was directly contrary to the uniform reports which the Company had been receiving for twenty years from the late Dr. Albert Leeds of Stevens Institute during his lifetime, and, after his death, from Dr. Ernest J. Lederle, both of whom were eminent bacteriologists. Dr. Leeds was a graduate of Haverford and Harvard who had received a Doctor of Philosophy degree in Germany, and was regarded during his lifetime as the country's leading authority on water analysis. Dr. Lederle was at one time Health Commissioner of New York City, and was the founder of Lederle Laboratories, which has become world famous as the developer of Aureomycin and other miracle drugs. Lederle's reports, moreover, were confirmed by independent laboratories to whom he sent samples of the water.

Mr. French's statement added that both scientific and popular opinion agreed that running water purified itself within a few miles. (This was a common view at the time, though not accepted today. There are natural processes of settlement, oxidation and sunlight which tend to lessen impurities in a stream, but the most effective of these involve time and storage rather than flow, because harmful bacteria die within a relatively few days in clear water away from their natural environment.) Mr. French had publicly stated six months before that the Company was going to build a filter plant, but pleaded that planning and building it would take time. What he did not say, or in any event what the papers did not print and doubtless would not have understood, was that the whole matter of water filtration was in a state of turmoil, with experts on both sides claiming that only their particular processes would work. The subject was still in a period of experimentation. In November, 1902, when the filtration affair was at its height, the Company had switched from the Hazen engineering firm, the leading proponents of slow sand filters, to the George W. Fuller firm. Messrs. Hering and Fuller had just built a plant at Louisville,

Kentucky, with a wholly new type of filter that required only two acres of filter bed to do a better job than one hundred and twenty-five acres would do in the Hazen system. The key to the new system was the use of coagulating basins in front of the filters, an expensive but highly efficient arrangement. On May 4, 1903, the Board of Directors approved the construction of a new filter plant using the Fuller system.

For the time being, French's efforts at public relations merely added fuel to the *Record's* fire. The paper placed his story back on page three and headlined it "Record Has Aroused Water Company," while repeating every accusation against the Company as if it were established fact, fact, which, it said, "refuted" Mr. French's statements. The paper added for good measure a reader's letter of general abuse of the Water Company and the Hackensack Board of Health. (The Board had refused to join in the attacks.) The fact that the Water Company had been making strenuous efforts to reduce pollution without fanfare, it was hinted, was an underhanded scheme to discredit its attackers. A long story followed in which a number of unnamed people, strategically located in the several towns of the county, were reported to be high in their praises of the paper for bringing the whole matter to public attention.

It cannot be denied that Mr. French did not help the case by his own attitude. He had a somewhat imperious air and little patience with small minds, and, we may be sure, even less patience with men who attacked his motives. When he stated that the planning and construction of a filtration plant would take time, he was not the man to debate the accuracy of his statement with a newspaper reporter. His answer to a junior who once told him that a prominent county official wanted a few loads of waste cinders for his driveway is still remembered fifty years later. The official, the junior explained, had much to do with granting street opening permits needed by the Company.

"How many loads does he want?", French asked.

"Three."

"How much do we charge for them?"

"A dollar a load."

"Tell him three dollars."

Having drawn a response from Mr. French, the paper now stepped up the level of abuse, calling for an indictment of the Water Company and running feature stories each day praising its own efforts to protect the lives of the people of the County while other newspapers pretended that all was well; and damning the Water Company officials for the rascals they were, their wickedness now compounded by their lying statements that the water was perfectly wholesome, when the *Record* had decided long since that it was not. The Board of Health of Hackensack and the Water Commissioners of Hoboken were pictured as fools for reporting that the water was safe, with broad hints that there was more behind the conduct of the two Boards than met the eye.

The *Hoboken Observer*, which of course did not compete with the *Record*, had joined in the attacks from the outset. Not everyone swallowed the stories whole. Several officials observed that there had never been a case of disease traced to the system. Water Commissioner Schmidt of Hoboken, a soda water bottler, may have reflected the general cynicism of knowledgeable Hoboken people when he observed that if the people who believed the stories didn't like the water they could drink Schmidt's Soda Water.

The other Bergen County papers, as might be expected, also took a somewhat detached view of their competitor's feature stories and the pronouncements of its ally, the county medical society, preferring to print reports from other sources that the water, though containing some organic matter, was perfectly wholesome.

A half century later we can see that the filtration affair, painful as it was to the Company, was an almost classic ex-

ample of the problems of Victorian men who found themselves
for the first time face to face with the beginnings of a new
world, a world where what you do counts for less than what
others think you do. The people who were guiding the Water
Company at the turn of the century thought of their work in
terms of their technical problems and their non-human objects,
partly because the very difficulty of the technical problems
they faced forced the question of customer approval into the
background. Mr. French and the other Company people were
concerned about building the reservoir that had to be finished
before a filtration plant could be built, about solving the engineering problems of slow sand filters and rapid-sand filters,
and about the technical problem of providing the best possible water, not about pleasing the newspaper-reading public.
However useful such single-minded men may be, they can be
most exasperating, and, as we have seen, not incapable of for-
getting to check whether the Carlstadt tank had been cleaned.
They were, of course, also blind to the possibility that if they
had kept the newspapers and the public better informed about
their plans and problems they would have been spared many of
their troubles. That was not the way businesses—or, to tell the
truth, newspapers—were run in those days.

* * *

On October 17, 1900, before the filtration controversy erup-
ted, the Company bought all of the outstanding stock of the
Spring Valley Water Works and Supply Company, a small
company in Rockland County, New York, founded by J. P.
Lespinasse, a local real estate developer, but at that time owned
almost entirely by F. B. Poor, George M. Dunlop and A. D.
Dunlop. The company's sole employee was an old man in town

who manned the pump and looked out for the property, and the stockholders were probably thoroughly tired of their troublesome investment. Mr. de Forest reported to the Board of Directors that it had been bought "in order to secure cooperation between that company and the Hackensack Company in protecting the watersheds from which both companies draw their source of supply from pollution."

We can be sure that no one could have imagined that the little half-bankrupt water company, whose first owner had to go around on Saturdays to try to collect water bills or sell stock so he could pay his employee his weekly wage, would over the years come to represent a large fraction of the whole Hackensack Water system. What Mr. de Forest did see was more important: that the Hackensack River and its tributaries had to be viewed as a unified watershed for public water supply with no regard for state lines, a piece of wisdom far ahead of the times, and, if we might judge by the agitation when the DeForest Lake Reservoir was built in the 1950's, far ahead of the times of many who lived a half century later.

Main Street Spring Valley, c. 1900
Post Card Collection of Mr. Gerry de la Ree

1903-1910

During the summer of 1903, the Water Company announced plans to build a large reservoir on Pascack Creek, at Woodcliff, New Jersey, five miles above the intake at New Milford. Though the reservoir had been planned long before, the need for additional storage was made obvious by a period of extreme drought in the spring of that year, when two months passed without rainfall and the woods were dry as tinder. At one time the pall of smoke from forest fires in New York and New England darkened the skies of New York City so badly that ships coming into the harbor lost their bearings, and, as one paper reported, ships at sea believed that the City itself "was on fire from end to end and about consumed." The Water Company found the Hackensack River at its intake nearly dry and was obliged to ask customers to save every possible drop of water.

Woodcliff, where the new reservoir was to be built, was a country town in 1903. Whereas row upon row of homes were being built in Hillsdale to the south and Park Ridge to the north, most of the conservative, well-to-do Jersey Dutchmen of Woodcliff had refused to sell their farms, and only a few of its 400 people were commuters. John H. Ackerman, the mayor, who ran the general store, P. Elvin Van Riper and David H. Tice, owners of large farms on Chestnut Ridge, and others like them, the men who dominated local affairs, were seemingly content to see the neighboring towns grow into busy commuting centers while Woodcliff remained a bucolic village, if indeed it could be called a village at all. Even the name of the place was controversial. Until a group of newcomers under the leadership of S. Burrage Reed persuaded the voters to make it a borough and call it Woodcliff, the village had borne the historic name of Pascack for two hundred years. Reed was a self-made man and a virtually self-taught architect, who had made a national repu-

Bridge over Pascack Creek, Woodcliff
Courtesy of Mr. Howard Durie

tation in his profession and was a man of great self-assurance, energy and drive. He had designed a number of New York City churches, several villas at Newport and many public buildings in other places, including the Passaic County Court House at Paterson. He had no patience with the mossbacks of the village who could not see beyond the ends of their noses and were perfectly content with an old-fashioned name and an old-fashioned town, and he had succeeded in ousting John Ackerman and the old Democratic leadership from power on that issue when the borough was incorporated. Though Ackerman had been quickly reelected mayor to succeed Reed, there were still hard feelings on the subject.

The little community and the neighboring town of Park Ridge were also in a turmoil over another matter, not related to politics. A few years before, a bearded, long-haired, somewhat uncouth-looking man in flowing robes, who called himself "Huntsman T. Mnason", set himself up in Park Ridge and began preaching a strange mixture of all of the far-out philosophies of the day: communal living, vegetarianism, health through religion and God's wrath at the sins of the day, generally combining violent attacks on his supposed enemies with pious calls for universal love. Local people thought they detected more evidence of particular affection for susceptible local girls than for mankind in general. Mnason's meetings, which often attracted as many as a thousand people, were bedlams, with Mnason shouting denunciations of the town and angry local people responding in kind. Converts among the ladies stood up and ripped the ruffles from their dresses and the flowers from their hats, and men, shouting that they were going straight to heaven, climbed the iron columns that supported the ceiling. They soon came to be called "Angel Dancers." After two unsuccessful efforts to keep Mnason in jail, some of the local people took direct action, dragging him out of his house, shearing one side of his shoulder-length hair and beard with horse-clipping shears and packing him off on the next train to New York, an episode for which one leading citizen, James Leach, the Nassau Street stationer, was prosecuted and heavily fined.

The next summer Mnason and his followers reappeared on Werimus Road in Woodcliff. He had persuaded two of his followers, Samuel and Mary Storms, to open their parents' home to them and to put their aged parents in a one-room outbuilding, where the father, a once prosperous farmer, was forced to cobble shoes for a living. Mnason proceeded to set up a communal enterprise on the Storms place, which he renamed the Lord's Farm. Sam Storms became "Simon the Pure" and Mary Storms became "Blaudina", taking their places along with "John the Baptist", "Titus the Pure", and other long-haired people in flowing robes. To the surprise of many who had forgotten the history of other such communal enterprises, the Angel Dancers turned out to be good truck farmers. Several of their neighbors, it is true, remarked on the wonderful profanity that some of the pious folk used while plowing, but others who were not put off by the wild appearance of the inmates often went there to buy vegetables. At one time "Mnason, Mary Storms, a woman by the name of Mary Howell and Garry Storms . . . were all locked up in the Hackensack jail charged with all sorts of weird practices; [at another] Mnason and the Howell woman were sent to State prison for a year, and the brother and sister, after having been incarcerated in the Hackensack jail for several months, were finally allowed their freedom." At intervals, Mnason and one or two other Angel Dancers would range out to threaten destruction to Hackensack or Paterson, where their eccentricities generally brought them into the police courts. Undaunted, it was Mnason's practice to lecture the courts on the proposition that he and his fellow-Angel Dancers were "God's children and those who persecute us had better take warning," pointing to the misfortunes, or coming misfortunes, of the two judges who had sentenced him to a term in the State Prison. At any rate, the Angel Dancers made good newspaper copy, whether they were in a local restaurant entertaining a new recruit who, to the amazement of his vegetarian hosts, proceeded to stuff himself with a huge steak, or in court for disturbing the peace, or the subject of speculation whether the relations between men and women on the Lord's Farm were not as communal as their property arrangements.

*   *   *

On June 7, 1903, the dry spell in New Jersey was broken by a heavy rain. As if to make up for the drought, rain fell on every day but one for the next three weeks until a total of 8.61 inches had fallen, the highest rainfall ever before recorded in the area during June. Rain or no rain, the Water Company set to work on the new Woodcliff reservoir and by August 10th, two hundred men were at work clearing the land and building the dam.

On October 8 and 9, 1903, the whole Hackensack Valley was inundated by the worst storm in history, a storm that is still remembered whenever northern New Jersey is flooded. All of the work was washed out completely, though the destruction of the partially built Woodcliff dam was the smallest of the Company's troubles. It started to rain on the morning of October 8, and, to quote a man who had driven from Bergenfield to Westwood that morning to attend an auction, it was "a measily rainy day all day." He thought little about it until he started home on the Flatts Road and saw a bridge he had just crossed go down the stream behind him, with the man in the following wagon, Orie Van Orden, the fish peddler, nearly carried downstream with it. By midnight almost six inches of rain had fallen. Lodi, Wallington, Peetzburg, New Milford, Oradell, Little Ferry and other places were submerged. The new bridge at Oradell was destroyed and most of the other bridges in the county were down. All of the local railroad and trolley lines were washed out. The Weehawken tunnel on the West Shore Railroad was closed by landslides. On the next day, the 9th, six more inches of rain fell, and by three o'clock in the afternoon there were twenty-five inches of water in the engine room of the New Milford Pumping Station, with the rain still coming down and the water rising. "The plant," the paper reported, "is surrounded by water [and] several men are held prisoner in the works. A large amount of lumber and material to be used in building the new filtering plant had been washed down the river, which has become a raging stream. . . . Few commuters reached New York, and those who did were hours getting home again, making the return by trolley, wagon or on foot." The Hackensack meadows were a broad expanse of water. On Friday, October 10, the fires at the pumping station had to be put out and the pumps were not put back into motion until the next Sunday morning, service being maintained by back flow from the reservoirs at Weehawken. Fortunately the dam at Oradell held fast, but two weeks later

Horsedrawn Dump Trucks Building Woodcliff Reservoir, 1904
Courtesy of Mr. & Mrs. John Fischer

the Company was still trying to pump out the filter plant excavations. The building materials were gone forever. A rope was raised above the river at the site of the old Oradell bridge north of the plant and workmen and others who had to cross the river there were ferried across on a rocking chair suspended from a pulley until a temporary pontoon bridge was built.

When the land dried out, large gangs of laborers went back to work at Woodcliff, clearing the land, hauling off dirt and building the high dam. Mr. John Ackerman, acting for the Water Company, had been able to arrange voluntary sales of

all of the land needed for the reservoir, and there were no problems of condemnation. Everything was going well. The project
promised to be a major civic improvement in the little village
and a much-needed source of water for the people of Bergen
and upper Hudson County. The first sign of trouble came
in early November, 1903, when the plan to relocate the few
roads affected by the reservoir was made public by the Mayor
and Council. The *Hackensack Republican*, which had stood
aside calmly enough while the *Record* trained its guns on the
Water Company during the filtration controversy, now found a
public service project of its own, the protection of the good
people of Woodcliff against the Water Company and the authorities of the village, old-line Democrats of the Garret Ackerson
type who still had a very large hand in running the County.
Eugene K. Bird, the editor of the *Republican*, was a fine old
professional newspaperman whose bark was worse than his bite,
a man who prided himself on his "peppery independence, salty
wit and satire acid as vinegar", as a contemporary newspaper
wrote of him. We may be sure that neither the Water Company
nor the Woodcliff officials saw much to admire in his acid pen.
The reservoir, the *Republican* announced on November 12,
1903,

> "will not only submerge a large territory but add a great in-
> convenience to the public by obliterating important public
> highways. A little further south—at Hillsdale and along the
> brook—people fear disaster from the big dam giving way
> under flood pressure. As at present reported, those in power
> treat the people with Vanderbiltian courtesy, ignoring their
> protests and refusing them a hearing."

What had evidently happened was that S. B. Reed, who
had succeeded in ousting Mr. Ackerman from office for a
short time a few years earlier, saw in the road relocation
plans an opportunity to stir up a new revolt against the

town's traditional leadership, with the help of two minority councilmen and the *Republican*. He was not mistaken, at least in believing that his old followers could produce a lively opposition if properly aroused. One unpleasant evening in mid-November, sixty people showed up at Reed's Hall, a barren, converted wood-working plant, "where [the *Republican* said] the kerosene lamps cheered the vale with hospitable rays," in response to a call "to confer together concerning the water reservoir . . . and many important matters connected therewith. An impending crisis confronts us! Are we prepared to meet it?" If the *Republican* was to be believed, they were indeed:

> "The Borough of Woodcliff, with a voting population of just one hundred, is in a state of agitation bordering upon a revolution. . . . Citizens of Woodcliff today feel as if they are struggling against as arrogant and overbearing a government as that represented by the red-coat satraps of the English monarch. . . . The present objectionable official is the Mayor, who is said to control the Council in every detail of its work, which is alleged to be all tending to benefit the official head of the borough. . . . For a wonder, the meek and lowly worms of the soil squirmed under the heavy heel of rough-shod authority and overbearing selfishness. . . ." (*November 19, 1903.*)

Some of the readers of this story perhaps were less moved by its purple prose than by the discovery, upon reading further, that one of the two nominal leaders of the revolt was an Angel Dancer from the Lord's Farm, an institution which had never before received such respectful treatment from the press, though the *Republican's* account would have done credit to Mnason himself at the height of one of his perorations against the wicked city of Paterson. The particular Angel Dancer, W. C. Musson, was no Mnason, and even the *Republican* could credit him at the meeting with nothing more pugnacious than the observation that "If a thing is not right, I think it could be changed." Even Mr. Reed was comparatively restrained. So far as he was concerned, he did not go along with the *Republican* in opposing the reservoir; he was complaining only about the changes in road locations. But there were others who were after Mr. Ackerman and the Water Company, horse, foot and dragoons:

John H. Ackerman General Store, Pascack (Woodcliff) 1873
Courtesy of Mr. and Mrs. John Fischer

"Lawyer W. W. Westervelt [the *Republican* said] . . . flayed the Mayor and Council right and left. . . . [He] charged Mayor Ackerman with being in league with a corporation that was going to swallow up the rights of the people, whether or no. . . . 'When the Mayor and Council say that no application has been made for a franchise, it is a lie, and I will prove it,' said Mr. Westervelt."

At this point Councilman Meyers, who had been watching the performance, walked out in anger. "Can our Mayor,"

Westervelt went on to ask after the interruption, "act as agent of a company which intends to inflict a wrong upon his borough . . . ?"

It was a fine speech, well calculated to please the people who had called the meeting, and, we may be sure, made not a whit less effective by the fact that the Water Company had applied for no franchise and needed none. When the meeting was about to close and the people in attendance were asked to sign up for the task before them, only twenty-six came forward. Most of the audience were evidently present out of curiosity.

Undiscouraged at finding only a quarter of the voters on his side, Reed called another meeting ten days later, when, the *Republican* said, "there were several vigorous speeches, including one by H. W. Collingwood, editor of the *Rural New Yorker*, who gave his neighbors some good views and excellent advice." As many older Bergen County people will remember, Collingwood's *Rural New Yorker* was a household fixture in those years, a journal dedicated to the proposition that its readers were being victimized by commission merchants, fertilizer companies, farm equipment manufacturers, shady advertisers in rural magazines and indeed virtually everyone they dealt with. It contained little news but tales of innocent readers mulcted by sharpers. No reader of the *Rural New Yorker* could doubt Mr. Collingwood's utter conviction that he alone stood between the tiller of the soil and a rapacious world, and we may be sure his efforts to protect the good people of his own neighborhood from a grasping public utility were equally sincere.

The next meeting of the Mayor and Council was held on Tuesday, December 1, 1903, again in Reed's Hall, so poorly heated against the winter cold by a pot-bellied stove that the Mayor and Council in their overcoats, the paper said, "looked like Peary fresh from the Arctic." The small audience included lawyer Westervelt, former Mayor Reed and W. C. Musson and W. Robert Johnson of the Lord's Farm. Lawyer John H. Ward was a spectator in the interest of the Citizen's Association. Although the *Republican* used the occasion to repeat its own abuse of the town fathers and the Company, little was done but to exhibit the plan proposed by the Company for the causeway which now crosses the lake.

The *Republican*, however, was pleased by the way things were going:

> "If there is anything hereabouts indicating that citizens are going to sit on their hurkies and permit a robber corporation to despoil them of their highways and other rights, the citizens are not aware of it. They had another meeting of their association Monday evening, when report was made regarding the last Council meeting, employment of Capt. Z. M. Ward & Son of Paterson as counsel to protect the people's interests, and the whole subject was dispassionately but firmly reviewed by gentlemen deeply concerned. It is evident that the Water company and its agents will find a wedge in the cogs as soon as they attempt any overt act tending to rob the people of their highways. It was rumored at this meeting that Mayor Ackerman talks of resigning."
> (*The Hackensack Republican, December 10, 1903*)

The cold weather of the next few months chilled the controversy for a while. On January 5, 1904, the thermometer dropped to 30 degrees below zero. Trains and trolleys were stalled, water pipes were frozen in the ground (the Water Company rebated bills for large numbers of customers), and the few commuters who braved the cold got frozen noses and ears for their trouble. The New York, Susquehanna and Western station at Hackensack was turned into an emergency hospital for frostbite cases. Plumbers and coal men made a fortune. "If the most humble plumber in town had 100 men," the *Record* said on January 7,

> "he could have kept them hustling yesterday and the day before. . . . If there were discomfitures, there were also

pleasures. Last night the inordinately cold weather, good bottom for sleighing and moonlight appealed to lovers of sleighing, and everything on runners was out. Hundreds of merry sleighing parties dashed about over country roads and enjoyed dances at the hotels."

On February 1, Woodcliff passed the formal resolution closing the old roads through the reservoir site and establishing the present causeway (a "new road on stilts," the *Republican* called it). The Mayor, "one of the largest property owners and most wealthy citizens of the borough," as the *Republican* observed, limited the discussion to people owning property on the roads that were to be abandoned. Since the Water Company owned all of the land in question, the small but vociferous group of dissidents were reduced to putting their personal objections on the record. The *Republican*, frustrated in its effort to protect the good people of Woodcliff from the indignity of a lake in the center of their village, closed its campaign with a malediction on

Causeway over Woodcliff Reservoir, 1905
Courtesy of Mr. and Mrs. John Fischer

the lake and its sponsors which would have done credit to the Angel Dancers themselves:

"The two ordinances are wholly in the interest of the Hackensack Water Company. The old roads are not to be abandoned until the new one is built. This is the only concession made to the people who want the old roads retained. It will save them from driving three or four miles around to reach their railroad station.

"A few persons are so complaisant as to feel that this is a blessing for which they should be grateful to the authorities who are depriving them of their rights.

"When the reservoir is built and the stagnant water converts Woodcliff into a summer resort with malaria as its leading allurement, every citizen will make a bequest to place a wreath of roses upon the grave of Mayor Ackerman at each recurrence of the anniversary of the passing of these ordinances.

"Should the dam now being built at Hillsdale Manor break and cause widespread destruction of life and property, those afflicted by such a disaster will add to the floral tributes a series of resolutions expressing their gratification with the Water Company's action in establishing the reservoir." (*The Hackensack Republican, February 4, 1904*).

The work went on nonetheless. On May 6, 1904, the *Record* carried an item from Hillsdale Manor under the headline "Water Man Saw Snakes," reporting that "Mr. Drury, bookkeeper for the Hackensack Water Company, was attacked in his office at that place . . . by a large black snake," four and a half feet long, which Mr. Drury found in a corner of his office, showing fight. With assistance Mr. Drury killed the reptile. "Some people," the *Record* went on, "may think it a strange place to see snakes in a water office. But reptiles are now crawling out to sun themselves, and two boys killed 60 [near the reservoir] last Sunday." The

Company's workmen, who were living in large temporary dormitories at both Woodcliff and New Milford, were also frequently mentioned in the press. Just as the sun went down on Sunday evening, August 29, 1904, the *Record* reported,

> "citizens of New Milford were greatly alarmed [by a] disturbance among the numerous laborers employed by the Hackensack Water Company in building the big reservoir at New Milford. The row started in a shanty occupied by a number of laborers . . . [One] flourished a razor in a reckless manner and wanted to carve up one of his fellow countrymen . . . [Another] jumped in as a peacemaker and . . . came dangerously near to losing his life. He was cut across the abdomen by the man with the razor . . . but the weapon struck against the ribs, which deflected it from reaching a vital spot. The injured man was removed to Hackensack Hospital, where he is said to be in a fair way to recover." *(Bergen Evening Record, August 30, 1904)*.

Hillsdale's zealous one-man police force had its own troubles with the laborers at the Woodcliff Reservoir. On December 14, 1904, Constable Rawson's keen eye spotted a workman who was carrying a gun and a dead rabbit, and pursued him briskly until the miscreant disappeared into a house where about forty of the laborers lived, and, the paper said, "as [they] all looked alike to Rawson, he was unable to pick out the poacher." Rawson had earlier caught and convicted two of them for fishing in the lake, and had been constantly at work all fall trying to keep them from washing clothes in the reservoir.

Another news story that fall concerned the mysterious death of James Sisco, one of the Company's construction foremen. Sisco, a descendant of a negro who had been a British spy in the area during the Revolution, and no newcomer to Bergen County, had gone coon hunting with six other men in the woods near Mayor Grant's place (that is to say, near the present Haworth filtration plant) at about 8 o'clock one Saturday evening in September, 1904. "They returned from the hunt about 10:45; had drinks at Wortendyke's Hotel . . . then separated; Sisco walking up the railroad tracks with his dog . . . toward his home at Hillsdale. He was not intoxicated and had no watch or money." Sisco's body was found the next morning, a half mile north

Westervelt Hotel, Oradell, Built 1872
Oradell Public Library

of the Oradell station, on the tracks opposite Lozier's horse farm, killed by a blow on the head. His murderer was never found.

*   *   *

During the Spring of 1905, when the Woodcliff Reservoir had been completed and opposition to it was almost forgotten, the people of the neighborhood received letters reading

"You are cordially invited to take part in the dedication services of the new reservoir of the Hackensack Water Company which takes place on Saturday, April 1, at the new dam, Hillsdale Manor, New Jersey. Trains will leave Cham-

General View of Woodcliff and Woodcliff Reservoir, c. 1905
Courtesy of Mr. Howard Durie

bers Street Ferry, New York, at 1:15, 1:30 and 3:23 P.M.
Music from 3 until 6 p.m. furnished by Lirpa Band."

Large numbers were on hand. "There were reporters there,
too, but they were on business, not pleasure. Just the same they
were looking for the music, or rather the promised lunch."
There was no dedication; it was all a rather expensive April Fool
joke, and, as the *Republican* said, the word "dam" was more
often used to refer to the prankster than the "new monster dam"
that held the water back.

A few months after the reservoir was finished, to quote Westervelt's *History of Bergen County*, it had "so transformed and
improved the general appearance of the place that the word 'lake'
was added to the name of the borough, making it Woodcliff
Lake." Whether the Angel Dancers or any of the other opponents of the reservoir stopped in at the general store of John H.
Ackerman to apologize for abusing him is of course no part of
the record. As a matter of fact, the death of Mary Storms at
about that time marked the beginning of the end for the

Angel Dancers:

> "Mary Storms, for many years the favorite of Huntsman T.
> Mnason, chief familiar at the Lord's Farm at Woodcliff, and
> one of the guiding spirits of the curious sect known as the
> 'Angel Dancers,' was buried yesterday in the Pascack
> cemetery of the Reformed church. Mary Storms was 39
> years of age, and the greater part of her life had been spent
> with the religious enthusiasts who form the colony of
> Woodcliff....
> "When she first joined the community, Mary Storms was
> quite a beauty. She was popular in the little world of
> Woodcliff, but her friends fell away from her, and for the
> last several years she has lived the life of a hermit on the
> Lord's Farm." (*The Evening Record, January 18, 1905.*)

Shortly after her death the Storms' relatives threw Mnason
out of the house and put her father back in possession, and the
Angel Dancers, beset by desertions and their other troubles,
disappeared.

*   *   *

Work on the filters at New Milford had continued while
Woodcliff Lake was under construction. By the end of 1904,
they were filled with about fifty carloads of specially-graded
sand from Sea Girt, "together," the *Record* reported on September 29, "with considerable charcoal and crushed stone, through
which purifying process the water will pass...." On January
20, 1905, seventy-five engineers attending the annual convention
of the American Society of Civil Engineers at New York went
to New Milford by special train to visit the plant:

> "It is something out of the ordinary, [the *Record* said]
> many novel features being introduced. There is only one
> other anywhere near like it and that is at Little Falls in Passaic County ... After an inspection of the plant the party

of engineers enjoyed a banquet on the ground floor of the building. As an employee went down to the river with a saw and axe and cut a wheelbarrow load of blocks of ice, it is presumed the engineers also took a survey of a cold bottle."

New Milford Plant after Construction of Filter Plant, c. 1906

If the Water Company people imagined that the cheerful story about the filter plant reflected a new attitude on the part of the press, they had only to wait for a few months to see how wrong they were. Even the most cynical of them would hardly have predicted the new attack. The *Record*, which a few years earlier had written story after story describing the indifference of the Hackensack Water Company to the pollution of its water supply, now began a series of articles attacking it for its arbitrary actions in making people remove privies from the banks of the stream and clean out cesspools that drained into the water supply. The *Record* felt that, since, as everyone knew, it was a rich corporation, it ought to buy the property of anyone who decided to pollute any of the hundreds of streams flowing into the reservoirs.

Boiler Room Crew at New Milford Plant, c. 1912

"Complaint is made by the Company to the State Board of Health that someone is violating the sanitary regulations of the owners of the water rights," the paper reported indignantly, though what the offender was actually violating was the State law, and then went on:

> "The State Board of Health sends word to the person in question that they must cease to pollute the stream under penalty of the law. Naturally enough a man who owned his home on the banks of the stream before the water company secured the water rights feels that he has as much right as the water company to do what he pleases." *(Bergen Evening Record, May 8 and 9, 1906.)*

J. C. Storms, publisher of the *Park Ridge Local*, was reported to be incensed. He had lived there for many years, and "no trouble had ever been known or heard of until the water company had made its advent. . . . If the company does not want their sewage let them move." Those who knew "Kippy" Storms understood that he was more interested in turning a phrase than in the current crusade, but strangers may have been impressed. The report continued: "James Leach, Mayor of Park Ridge, a follower of Fremont, the Pathfinder, a highly esteemed resident of the place, said that his experience with the Hackensack Water Company was not of a kind to kindle in his bosom a long and lasting love for that corporation." The experience of the esteemed disciple of Fremont the Pathfinder was that he had been ordered by the courts, at the suit of the State Board of Health, to remove a privy from the edge of Bear Brook, which ran directly into the reservoir. The newspaper campaign ended after a few issues, but we may be sure that D. W. French, for one, who had borne the brunt of the earlier attacks on the Company, did not fail to comment to his friends on this new proof of the depth of the commitment of the County's press to the cause of pure water. Of course, the stories proved nothing whatever about the paper's interest or disinterest in pure water. What they reflected was a decision of a harried editor who had before him an interesting if somewhat biased story about a local controversy, and a deadline an hour or two away. Mr. French was fortunate that he was not obliged to accept or reject water on a moment's notice, as the editor was obliged to accept or reject news.

* * *

On June 25, 1906, the new filter plant was formally opened before a large gathering at which Dr. Ernest J. Lederle made an address in which he highly praised the new plant. The papers reported that "The filtration plant was inspected with great interest by those present, and a fine luncheon was served." Standard texts on water supply engineering now refer to the New Milford filter plant, along with Louisville, Kentucky, and Little Falls, New Jersey, as one of the great pioneering plants in the field, one of the plants which laid the groundwork for most of the later filter plants in the nation.

* * *

During the years at the beginning of the century, several new men had been elected to the Board of Directors who were to have a long connection with the Company. William M. Johnson, Esq., for four decades perhaps the leading citizen of Bergen County, was elected in 1897 and served for over thirty years. He was a leader of the New Jersey bar, the founder of the Hackensack Trust Company, one of the founders of the Hackensack Hospital and the Bergen County Historical Society, and State Senator for many years. He is perhaps best remembered today as the donor of the Johnson Public Library in Hackensack. Mr. Hamilton F. Kean took the place of his uncle Julian Kean at the Annual Meeting in 1904; Mr. D. W. French, after more than twenty years as an employee, joined the Board in 1906; Mr. Alexander M. White, the Company's investment banker, a man, like Robert deForest, having wide interests in charitable enterprises, was elected in 1907, and was succeeded two years later by his nephew, Harold T. White (who was to serve for over fifty years, many of them as Chairman of the Board); Mr. Henry L. deForest (who later became Chairman of the Board and President), son of Robert W. deForest, was elected in 1911.

If Robert deForest or any of the other directors of generous spirit had been concerned about D. W. French while he was bearing the brunt of the newspaper attacks about the filter plant and the destruction of the privies of the unfortunate people along Pascack Creek, they would have been edified to know the whole story of the experiments that preceded the construction of their New Durham Pumping Station, which was being built at the same time as the filter plant and Woodcliff Lake Reservoir. Mr. French was reasonably able to take care of himself.

The New Durham Pumping Station produced no newspaper stories, but it was of great interest to waterworks engineers. About eighty per cent. of the system's water was then being pumped fifteen miles from the New Milford plant, ten feet above mean high water, to the two distributing reservoirs at Wee-hawken, at elevations of nearly two hundred feet, from which it was distributed to Hoboken and the north Hudson County towns. For reliability, three separate mains were used to supply these reservoirs. Using separate routes to the head of the Hackensack meadows, they then ran parallel at a low elevation along the public highway at the eastern edge of the meadows, and thence up the hill to Weehawken. In the summer of 1903, daily consumption steadily exceeded 17,000,000 gallons. Knowing that it would take the best part of two years to build a proposed new 48-inch line from New Milford to supplement the supply, D. W. French conceived the idea that a relay pumping station

Mr. and Mrs. D. W. French at right and E. H. Cate, c. 1906
Mr. French was Superintendent and Manager from 1886 to 1928
Mr. Cate Was an Officer of the Company at the Time

The New Durham Pumping Station

White Motor Company Steam Touring Car Purchased in 1905
Courtesy of White Motor Company

situated at precisely the right point on the line could double its capacity quickly and avoid the need for a new line. It was imperative, however, to get reliable data concerning the maximum amount of water that the New Milford station could deliver to the proposed relay point. Mr. French described his method of ascertaining the facts in a paper he delivered at the American Water Works Association in 1906, where, presumably, there were no reporters present. He first installed two 12-inch blow-offs in one 36-inch main at the proposed relay point.

"Knowing that a considerable quantity of water drawn from the blow-offs would submerge many acres of the low adjacent flatlands and possibly cause some embarrassment in answering questions, it seemed worth while to wait for a suitable opportunity before opening the gates, and, if possible, to appear to throw some of the responsibility for complaint elsewhere. [When, therefore, a rain of over two inches fell on a Saturday night] and with the country well afloat anyway, it seemed . . . that it was a most opportune time to open the 12-inch gate."

The speed of the New Milford pumps was increased, and, as Mr. French had predicted, without the load of the line running up the Palisades twice as much water was delivered through the same mains at the selected point at New Durham. He added that "all of the visiting friends and relations of the New Durham natives continue to hear the wonderful 'cloud-burst' story which all but swept the town away one Sunday some two and a half years ago."

Having proved that the three existing mains could deliver the water, he convinced the directors not to go ahead with the 48-inch line, but to build a relay station. When it was completed and put in service in 1904, it worked like a charm. The old Florentine water tank at Weehawken was taken out of service, the customers in Hudson County were spared a water shortage and Mr. French was able to deliver his learned paper to his fellow-engineers.

New Durham Pumping Station, c. 1909

Mr. French, a handsome, aristocratic figure, the son of a poor New England shoemaker, was a man who had educated himself by his own efforts and risen to a leading position in his profession. Serious to the point of regarding the Hackensack Water Company as his personal responsibility and his personal property, the people of Hudson, Bergen and Rockland Counties owe him a debt which can hardly be measured, for he almost singlehandedly forced through long-term projects which have supplied millions of people with water that would have been lost if he had been seeking public acclaim. Even within the Company he was probably held in far more respect than affection.

Sixty years later there are a few who still remember with some pleasure his troubles with early automobiles, which did not wholly yield to his strong personality. Though he was a steam-oriented engineer, he was talked into trying an electric machine which did not work at all, possibly because he had little confidence in electric motors. By no means the only engineer of the day who considered electricity or steam preferable to the internal combustion engine, he then bought a beautiful White Steamer, which he kept polished like one of his walnut and brass-trimmed Worthington pumps, but he was far too impatient to wait twenty minutes for the boilers to heat up and, worse, to stop every few miles for water. He was finally persuaded to try a gasoline automobile. He told the salesman that he would have to be shown before he bought one. When the car arrived at Weehawken, Mr. French came out for a test ride, but it could not be started. A second car was sent and driven to Hackensack before it too broke down. Nevertheless, the Company bought a gasoline motor car, which ran reasonably well, so well in fact that Mr. French undertook to carry a number of directors from Weehawken to New Milford for an inspection trip soon after. He had hardly started along the street in front of the office when he reached across the seat for a map of transmission lines and had the bad luck to run into one of the few other cars for miles around, which happened to be parked at that point. The trip was abandoned.

On October 1, 1908, Mr. French added another individualist to the payroll, though at the time he may have thought him merely stubborn. Sixteen-year old Emile J. Fricker, who lived in a neighboring Hudson County town, came into the office and asked for a job as a stenographer. Mr. French needed a secretary, and was so impressed by the youngster that he offered him the job, with a salary of $30 a month. Emile had had in mind $35 a month and said so. Mr. French declined the counter-offer, and, not realizing that he had met his match in horse-trading, proceeded to negotiate. The matter was finally settled at $35 a month when Emile suggested that as a compromise he would work the first week for nothing. Considering that the first week was about .0004% of the time that Mr. Fricker worked for the Company, his concession was perhaps less than Mr. French had calculated. D. W. French did not know that in Emile J. Fricker he had met one of those extraordinary men who had the ability to say no in a trade and leave the man on the other side with the impression that he had just received a great concession. Mr. French may never have realized it, because Emile Fricker had the equally rare faculty of leaving everyone with whom he dealt fully assured of his eminent fairness.

Mr. Fricker has always been fond of illustrating this fairness with a story about one of his land purchases. Many years ago, when the Company was rounding out its protective lands near the Woodcliff Reservoir, he asked John Ackerman to sell a piece of land just west of the reservoir on which there was a small old house. Mr. Ackerman refused on the ground that a colored man who had been with the Ackerman family for many years lived there at a rent of $5 a month, and would find it very hard to get other quarters at any such price. Picturing a bent-over family retainer living out his declining years, Mr. Fricker said that that was no problem, the Water Company would buy the house and let him stay there as long as he lived at the same rent. Mr. Ackerman was happy to sell on that basis and they started back over the causeway to sign the contract, when Mr. Ackerman pointed to a man going in the same direction who had just passed their car at high speed on his bicycle and said, "As a matter of fact there he is now." After many years of $5 a month rent, the tenant died and the house was torn down.

1911-1916

During 1911, the Spring Valley Water Works and Supply Company, which had been serving the Village of Spring Valley and a few nearby houses in the town of Ramapo for the last twenty years, was approached by the Villages of Piermont and Grandview and the Town of Orangetown about a possible extension to the Hudson River, a distance of about ten miles from the Spring Valley pumping station. The Company was happy to make the extension, and proceeded to lay about twenty-five miles of twenty-inch and twelve-inch trunk line across Rockland County. The cost of the project, which was completed in 1913, was nearly fifty times the original cost of the little Spring Valley Company, all of the money being advanced by the parent Company against the delivery of Spring Valley's bonds, which until recent years paid no return whatever.

The first appearance of Mr. Henry L. deForest in the Water Company's affairs occurred at this time. He was the son of Robert W. deForest, had been a member of the first graduating class of the Hotchkiss School, went on to Yale to become one of her great athletes (he was offered a big-league contract as a baseball player when he graduated), attended Columbia Law School, went to Duluth, Minnesota, to practice law for a number of years, and then returned to the family law firm, deForest Brothers, in New York City, whose successor, Messrs. deForest & Duer, still act as counsel of the Company, one of its senior

Launching Barge "Reliance,"
Oradell Reservoir, 1911
Courtesy Mr. Edwin D. Veldran
(Mr. Veldran is the Boy in Knickers)

partners, Robert W. Mulreany, being General Counsel of the
Company. Mr. deForest remembered to the day of his death
his troubles with each of the property owners along the right-
of-way to the Hudson, and the accusations that the pipe line
was nothing but a scheme to carry water to New Jersey. Henry
deForest had a long memory for other things as well. He found
it hard to think of the town of Hackensack without bringing
back to mind the strong suspicion that when the Yale University baseball team visited the town and played the Oritani
Field Club fifty years before, not all of the men in Oritani uni-
forms were local amateurs.

* * *

The Hackensack Water Company was now pumping out
an average of twenty-five million gallons of water a day, and it

was becoming obvious that steps would have to be taken to increase the capacity of the system, both by enlarging the pumping station and filter plant and by increasing the storage capacity of the Oradell Reservoir.

In 1911, the Company started to work on both projects, with Myles Tierney and his son John C. Tierney as general con-

Expansion of New Milford Plant, 1911

tractors. Woodchoppers were put to work clearing several square miles of low land north of the small existing reservoir, and a timber crib dam was built to raise the level of the water sufficiently to float a large barge, which was built on the west bank of the lake, christened the "Reliance" (after the America's

Cup yacht of that year) and launched with some ceremony. A 12-inch suction pump was assembled on the barge and set to work at dredging the lake. It succeeded so well that Mr. Tierney commissioned the construction of a much larger 20-inch dredge, which was soon at work alongside the *Reliance*. John C. Tierney, who had just completed construction of a mile-long tunnel for the Portland, Maine, water supply, was in charge of the

Twelve-inch and Twenty-inch Suction Dredges
on Oradell Reservoir, c. 1912

work, with a temporary office in the old Veldran Mill. The two dredges worked night and day, with the day crew working ten hours and the night crew twelve. Some of the crew lived on the Flatts Road near the present Haworth Filter plant, and Mr. Melvin King remembers that one of his jobs at the time was to ferry the others back and forth from Oradell in a Company motorboat. He also remembers that John Tierney went up to one of the barges late one night and found the entire twelve-man crew asleep, with the engines running briskly and the whole scene brilliantly floodlighted, but with the suction line taking up river water. Mr. Tierney dismissed them on the spot. He had been very pleased up to that point with his scheme for paying bonuses for dredging more than a fixed quota.

Late one night, before the new dam had been sheathed with wood, a neighbor woke Mr. King to tell him that the dam had sprung a leak. Mr. King was able to round up two of the men

Vertical High Service Pumps, Installed 1911

who worked on the dredging operation, go up about a mile to the Lozier boathouse and sail a barge with a steam shovel down to the dam and repair it before the whole structure collapsed.

On February 22, 1913, William V. V. Mabon, of Hackensack, twenty-two years old, the Company's "Clerk of the Works," went over to the east side of the lake to check on the woodchoppers, who were paid by the cord to fell and cut up the standing timber. He decided to take a short-cut back by walking the pipes to the west side of the lake, and fell, breaking through the soft ice. Rescuers who heard his shouts and saw him struggling were unable to approach him and he died, evidently from a heart attack brought on by exertion rather than by drowning. Mr. Melvin King, his assistant, was promoted to his place.

The dredging operations, which continued up to 1916, stirred up a good deal of mud in the river, mud which put a heavy burden on the filters, and even after filtration, left a cloudy residue in the water which had no effect on its wholesomeness but certainly did little to please customers. There were also frequent reports from customers of "red water".

A Hackensack resident who complained to his plumber about the cloudy water was told that it came from alum in the water. The customer, who could have found the facts quickly enough by asking the Water Company what caused the cloudiness, chose instead to write to a Dr. Wiley, a well-publicized newspaper food expert of the day, to see if alum was dangerous. This expert quickly replied that alum would be very injurious to health if present in any quantity in the water, and went on to deliver a dissertation on water filtration, in which he took the firm position that it was wrong to add alum after precipitation of the suspended material in the water. The good doctor may or may not have known that this piece of wisdom was nonsense, since the aluminum sulphate which was used in water filters to coagulate the impurities in the water had to be added before and not after precipitation, since it was the alum that caused the precipitation. He also may or may not have known that the coagulant product was easily and completely removed by settlement and filtration. Whether he did or not, the letter served the immediate purpose of persuading the casual reader that a real expert was now at work on a problem which had hitherto escaped the attention of scientists and water supply experts. When the customer received Wiley's alarming reply he went directly to the Hackensack Board of Health to demand that the threat to the public health be removed at once. The Board itself was not much impressed, but a reporter for the *Record*, which had been demanding filtration ten years earlier, now took up arms against the process. The President of the Board tried to allay concern by saying that the impression that there was something wrong was caused by the bad odor and discoloration of the water, which in turn was caused by the dredging at its source, and not by alum.

Dr. Humphrey, another member of the Board, was even more outspoken than the President. He offered to check the water in his own laboratory, observing that though it was perhaps an injustice to Dr. Wiley to attribute statements to him without reading his actual letter, Dr. Wiley was no scientist. Pressed somewhat further, Dr. Humphrey said plainly that Wiley was an excellent politician and in the doctor's opinion might be termed a scientific crook, at which the President, unused to such plain talk, asked the press to forget what they had heard. The paper instead published, in so many words, Dr. Humphrey's unkind comments on the food expert, and then went on to write a story which left the impression that the food expert was right, that there was indeed good cause for worry about the town's water supply, and that the Board of Health was guilty of trying to suppress the truth about the unwholesome water. The Water Company people, who remembered the trouble that the newspapers had created ten years before, could easily see what lay before them if a campaign was started to persuade the public that their water supply was full of alum and dangerous to health. Their worries left out of account George R. Spalding, the short, handsome, cheerful, peppery 32-year-old Yankee, positive in speech and obviously competent, who had recently become the Company's Chief Chemist. George Spalding did not mean to sit at home and let a food-faddist attack the quality of the water he sent out to the public.

He had graduated from M. I. T. a few years before and gone to work for the Lederle Laboratories, the firm which had been checking the quality of the Hackensack Water Company's water

Swimming at Eden Beach on West Side of
Hackensack River, River Edge, c. 1910
Courtesy of Mr. and Mrs. Fred W. Bogert

for many years. He worked for a time for the East Jersey Water
Company at Little Falls, but was persuaded by Mr. deForest or
Mr. French to come and take charge of the new chemical laboratory at the New Milford plant. There he spent the rest of
his business life, one of the men to whom millions of people owe
a debt of gratitude of which they are completely oblivious. At
the next meeting of the Board of Health, George Spalding, who
could hardly wait for the routine business of the Board to end,
proceeded to put on a performance that ended, once and for all,
the nonsense about alum in the water.

"The meeting room", the *Record* reported on February 21,
1913, "looked very much like a chemist's laboratory, with large
and small bottles, acids, etc., spread over the tables." Spalding,
with a self-assurance and a strong Yankee accent which carried
utter conviction, lectured the meeting "on the source, plant, filtration, etc., with the result that a small audience learned many

148

things regarding the water supply to this town". Mr. Spalding explained that the clouded water was caused by traces of earth deposits resulting from the recent dredging, that the "flavor" was imparted by hypo-chloride of lime, the chlorinating agent then used, and that the "red water" was due to rust in the customers' own boilers and pipes. He explained that 600 plants in the United States used rapid sand filters with alum coagulators, while only twenty of the old slow sand filters without coagulators were still operating. Having first referred to Dr. Wiley's statement that alum in water is dangerous, Mr. Spalding agreed. "I wouldn't drink water myself with alum in it. But I am going to prove to you there is no alum in the Hackensack water when it reaches the householder, although it is used in the filtration process." He tested the distilled water, added a trace of alum and showed the results, and then compared the samples with a glass of water taken from a faucet in the room, and showed it to be as free of alum as the distilled water. A few cynical listeners were not convinced, but everyone else at the meeting gave Mr. Spalding a vote of thanks by acclaim, and asked him to repeat his talk and experiment for the edification of the State Street School. When, a few days later, the *Record* recovered from George Spalding's coup, it fell back on the complaint that no one really knew the facts after "the mass of words and technical terms," but there was no doubt in anyone's mind that George Spalding had met the enemy and they were his. The alum scare was as dead as a doornail.

The muddy water in the river was a different case. Neither George Spalding nor anyone else was able to do anything about the complaints of downstream people about that.

> "People from other cities visit these places with the intention of having a few days enjoyment on the river and taking a plunge occasionally, but their plans are spoiled, for the water is not clean enough for a dog to swim in. When folks

Company Outing 1935
Emile J. Fricker (center) and
Jules Von Scheidt (left)

come from the city and see this stream of muddy water, they return a bit disgusted and tell their friends of it. In this way property owners, railroads and pleasure resorts along the river lose a large amount of money and people of the city are deprived of having a few days' pleasure in that place."

(To a modern reader it is perhaps more remarkable that the Hackensack River was once clear enough at River Edge, New Milford and North Hackensack for people to swim in than that it was temporarily muddied by dredging.) The complaints continued throughout the whole summer of 1913; indeed the files of deForest Brothers indicate that the Company was much concerned over suits for silting up the channel below New Milford. Efforts were made to isolate the dredging areas from the main reservoir with some success, but nothing really improved the situation until the enlarged reservoir was finally finished.

*   *   *

Between 1890 and 1910, Hudson County had doubled its already large population, and thinly-settled Bergen County had increased its population by three hundred per cent. The Water Company moved its lines northward into Hillsdale, Harrington Park and Norwood, and was constantly at work extending its mains in the towns it already served. The Erie Railroad praised Bergen County as the "Mecca of suburban dwellers," asserting that those who moved there would have "their childen and their children's children rise up and call them blessed." Trolley lines crisscrossed Hudson County and the lower parts of Bergen County. The first commuters had been the wealthy or the extraordinarily energetic but by 1910 multitudes began to establish themselves in the commuting towns. Hudson County, no longer a commuting area, filled up even more densely, largely with the new immigrants who had arrived by the tens of thousands during the last two decades. By 1910 only 39.8 per cent. of the people of New Jersey were descended from native-born parents. John T. Cunningham's "*New Jersey; America's Main Road*" estimates that 30 to 50 per cent. of these immigrants were illiterate, even in their native language. In West Hoboken (now part of Union City), the Company served a five-block section known as the Dardanelles because it held within its narrow boundaries Armenians, French, Germans, Greeks, Italians, Syrians, Rumanians, Polish, Russians, Chinese, Japanese, Austrians, Swiss and Jews; and virtually every town in the Company's territory had a section, under one name or another, where newly arrived immigrants predominated, Little Italy, Little Hungary or Little Sweden in many towns, Texas in Englewood, Paradise in Bergenfield, Hudson Street in Hackensack. Hard working men, who had truly come to America so that their children and their children's children might call them blessed, one could hardly blame these strangers in a new land for being suspicious, imposed upon as they were by their employers, by their own leaders and by most of the people they dealt with, and of course by the politically ambitious.

Emile Fricker remembers an incident in which the Company innocently added to the troubles of one newly-arrived resident of Fairview. Mr. Fricker came downstairs at the Weehawken office one day and saw an Italian friend of his named Tony, dressed in his Sunday best, standing in front of the window where applications for service were filed. Tony had built a house with his own hands at Fairview and, at Emile Fricker's suggestion, had dug a long trench through the rocky ground to reach the Company's nearest main to save expense. Mr. Fricker greeted him warmly, went to the counter and asked the clerk to do everything possible to help get the water line into service quickly, and went out. Unfortunately, the lady behind the window was a former school teacher who believed that an application for service was a serious matter, and in cases where the applicant could not read, insisted on reading the two pages of fine print to him. When Mr. Fricker returned a half hour later, his friend at the window was standing with a baffled look on his face, but seemingly patiently, while the lady droned out the long-winded legal verbiage printed on the back of the form. Thinking he might be able to help, Mr. Fricker went up to the window and said "Tony, how are you doing?" Tony glared at him a minute, pulled off his hat, threw it on the floor, jumped on it, shouted: "Mr. Frick, I think I sell the God-damn house," and stalked out of the office. Meanwhile the clerk kept on reading as if nothing was happening. In due time Tony's house was connected to the lines.

When Woodrow Wilson became Governor of New Jersey, he enacted a number of long-overdue reform bills that had been advocated by George L. Record, a tall, lanky down-Maine Republican transplanted to Jersey City, a most useful citizen who was not displeased to be likened to Abraham Lincoln. One of these bills established a Public Utilities Commission to regulate the rates and practices of New Jersey's powerful railroad, transit, electric and gas utilities, in emulation of the Commission that Governor Charles Evans Hughes had established in New York.

Emile J. Fricker, Assistant to President,
later Vice President 1928-1957

Whether deserved or not, many New Jersey utilities had a reputation running back into the first days of the railroads for controlling the state government and worrying very little about their customers. Unlike the New York law, the New Jersey law included water companies in its scope, though they were relatively small and certainly not politically powerful. Water Company officials, who were convinced that their own decisions about rates and service were just and reasonable, probably were not overjoyed to be subjected to the control of state commissioners. They were soon to learn that Public Utilities Commissioners were far better judges of utility rates than politicians seeking public office, who would certainly have endeavored to fix the rates if there had been no Commission.

It was a day when the public was aroused about trusts and monopolies. Theodore Roosevelt had made a name for himself in that field and Wilson was well on the way to doing the same. The railroads had recently raised their commuting fares twenty per cent, and complaints were heard on every side about electric and gas bills. To the great distress of the *Record*, the public seemed to think that the Water Company rates were fair, despite its annoyance with other utilities:

> "As we have pointed out repeatedly in these columns, the commuter howls about his railroad fare, the consumer about increased express charges, the householder about the high gas and electric rates, but no one seems to have anything to say about the Water Company. Just why this concern is treated as a thing of beauty and a joy forever passeth man's understanding."

A number of local politicians took the hint, and determined to set matters right by howling about water bills, too. Members of the County Board of Freeholders sprang into action with publicity releases, and an assemblyman named Kuhlke, from Hudson County, introduced a bill in the legislature to require all water companies to reduce their rates in Hudson County from $1.75 per thousand gallons, which he said was the existing rate, to $1.25 per thousand gallons. He "called upon the members of the House to vote for the bill in the interest of the common people," a plea that no politician could hear unmoved. A number of Bergen County assemblymen tried to jump aboard this project, so obviously calculated to please, by extending the benefits of the bill to Bergen County. Senator Charles O'Connor

Hennessey, of Bergen, an outspoken Wilson progressive and no friend of any utility, stood up in the Senate and opposed Kuhlke's bill (which had passed the assembly with only three negative votes) on the ground that it by-passed the new Public Utilities Commission and was manifestly unfair, since neither he nor anyone else in the legislature "was in a position to say ... whether the Water Company's rates fixed in Mr. Kuhlke's bill were too high or too low." The point had little relevance to the case so far as Mr. Kuhlke and his supporters were concerned, but Hennessey was successful.

Blocked by Hennessey's move, a large group of local officials now turned their thoughts to the Public Utilities Commission, the body charged by law with fixing fair rates and setting up service standards. Freeholder Brestel, it is true, grumbled at having to "initiate proceedings through the Public Utilities Commission to force a reduction of rates through the more tedious process provided under the Public Utilities Act which provides for hearings and the taking of testimony," but even he was reconciled to letting the Company present its side of the case if nothing else could be done. Public utility regulation was new, and no one knew much about it. The Company for its part was nervous about having a small group of political appointees decide what it was going to charge for its services after a half century of running its own affairs. Its opponents, on their part, were not sure whether they were entering upon a judicial proceeding or a political campaign, and instinctively assumed that the new Commission was going to decide the matter on the basis of newspaper attacks and public resolutions. The Commission, on its side, was anxious to act as a quasi-judicial body, but despite its pleas that a single letter would be enough to start an investigation, several leaders of the opposition proceeded to go about the territory beating the publicity drums against the wicked Water Company as if nothing else would stir the Commission into action. Some of the publicity may have been necessary to get public approval for spending large amounts for legal fees in a Commission case, and was to that extent justified, however distasteful it was to the recipients of the attacks. Most of the lawyers who were making speeches against the Company had no personal animus in the case and would have been far happier to be retained in a more professional way, and the Company should have taken some comfort from the fact that the speeches were often even more vehement in their demands that trolley fares be reduced to three cents than in their attacks on water rates. In any case, virtually every town in the Company's territory decided to join in the application. Whether the multitude of town lawyers was a help or a hindrance to the Commission is perhaps best left unanswered; it certainly furnished a good deal of local employment. Fifteen Bergen and Hudson County lawyers were in the case to the end.

For the Company's part, we may be sure that it felt that it was the victim of a horde of politically ambitious rascals and ambulance-chasing lawyers, and threatened with destruction by bureaucracy. The truth was that the rate case forced it to make an organized, rational study of its rate structure and performed a thoroughly useful purpose. With the rough and ready bookkeeping of those days, it was as likely as not that the Company, though it believed it was making a reasonable profit, was actually losing money on its business if non-cash expenses like depreciation and debt discount and expense were taken into account. (There is good reason to think that similar mistakes in those years are one of the reasons for the present troubles of the railroads.) As it turned out, the Company was right in assuming that it was making a reasonable over-all profit, but common sense more than financial data had produced the result.

Unmoved by the public speeches, the Commission set to work in a thoroughly competent way to study the whole subject. A joint property study was made by Dr. Philander Betts, the Commission's Engineer, and Nicholas S. Hill, the engineer retained by the Company for the purpose, a study which was so carefully done that it continues to this day to be the basis for recording the property owned at that time. The results of the Commission's study were reflected in its decision dated April 28, 1917, a model of a careful rate-making report, though perhaps not wholly pleasing to the Company. The Commission set up a uniform system of rates in place of the hodge-podge that had been established over the years as the Company went into the different towns, a move that the Company should have welcomed. No basis whatever was found for the claims of exorbitant rates. It is true that the average householder's charges were reduced, but the charges for hydrants, which had hitherto been an even livelier political issue than household rates, and much used as an example of "mulcting the public", were increased. The net result of the protracted case was to reduce the Company's revenues very little if at all. The low charge to Hoboken, and Hoboken's even lower charges to its own residents, were inferentially criticised. The most notable thing about the decision was the establishment of perhaps the first rational basis for hydrant rentals, the so-called "inch-foot charge", which Mr. Hill and Dr. Betts worked out to reflect the true costs of providing hydrant service. That determination alone was worth all of the trouble that the case involved. The 1917 case was the first of many in which the Water Company had reason to thank its lucky stars that it was regulated by a professional commission with an expert staff and not by the public speeches of lawyers and politicians. The customers could be equally thankful, for it would have profited them very little in the long run to allow politicians to bankrupt the Company that supplied them with water.

In June, 1915, during the rate case, Mr. Robert deForest brought in an engineer from the west coast to strengthen the executive staff at Weehawken. Earle Talbot, a Stanford engineering school graduate with a distinguished record in America and abroad, notably in Korea, where he designed and built several large dams, came to the Company as Secretary and Treasurer. He served in those offices, and as a Vice President, until his retirement in 1947. Like Mr. deForest himself, a gentleman of the old school, no one who had anything to do with the Water Company in the last fifty years could fail to be impressed with Earle Talbot, as far removed from the public conception of a rough and ready utility man as it is possible to conceive.

Aside from rates, there were complaints in many communities that hydrant pressures were low, and with the tremendously increased demands on the system, many of the complaints were probably justified. One such instance of lack of pressure occurred at a fire in a film studio at Fort Lee during the days when that place was the moving picture capital of the world. The story is probably of more interest today for its description of the early movies than for the regrettably small stream put out by the Company's hydrant, and deserves repetition:

> "Miserable and insufficient water pressure by the Hackensack Water Company was the real cause of damage to the plant of the Eclair Moving Picture Company at Fort Lee yesterday afternoon that will reach to about $500,000. The negative department where the machinery was located, together with the storage vaults, were destroyed. . . .
> "Among the productions destroyed were "The Cabellero's Way" just completed, in three reels, by the Arizona Company, and valued at $20,000, and one just received from Paris, "Protea," in six reels and which cost $60,000 to produce. Despite the fact that this separate structure was considered to be fireproof, it was completely destroyed. Just how it started no one seems to know, but Arthur Edison, one of the movie photographers, said:
> 'The stream of water from the nozzle would not carry six feet above us, and had we had even a half decent pressure

First Rate Case

Earle Talbot,
Vice President, Secretary and
Treasurer, 1915-1947

we could have put the blaze out in a few minutes. We even climbed to the roof of the scenery storage building and tried to throw the water across the open space of ten feet to where the flames were, but even this could not be done. Before the firemen reached the scene the whole factory was doomed. Half an hour later the auto chemical pumping engine came from Edgewater, but the damage had been done.' The studio was filled with actors who were rehearsing "The Gentleman of Mississippi," in which Thomas Wise is featured. All hands hurried from the studio and did what they could to aid in saving of property. . . .

"Henry Maire, the factory manager, almost wept as he looked on the fire while his own men endeavored to extinguish the first blaze with a stream of water that refused to go six feet in the air. He ordered one of his movie operators to take 900 feet of film of this stream so that he can offer it to the authorities and to the officials of the Hackensack Water Company. Mayor White, of Fort Lee, arrived on the scene while the blaze was at its height and he denounced the water service and pressure in bitter terms. . . .

"The Eclair Company has one of the best equipped plants in this country, their several buildings covering two square blocks. The factory building was built three years ago at a cost of $20,000 and was supposed to be fireproof. As late as Wednesday night the Fort Lee Council adopted resolutions condemning the excessive rates of the Hackensack Water Company and the insufficient pressure, and Mayor White produced a copy of the resolution to Manager Maire as the flames ate up many thousand dollars worth of material in the moving picture factory.

" 'We will start to rebuild our factory tomorrow,' said Mr. Maire last night." (*The Evening Record, March 20, 1914.*)

The producer whose pictures were thus destroyed left little imprint on the art of the moving picture (not, we may hope, because his greatest classics were lost in the fire), but there were many other moving picture people at Fort Lee who became famous, D. W. Griffith, for example. Mack Sennett, Mary Pickford, Pearl White, Fatty Arbuckle, Norma Talmadge, Irene Castle and Warner Oland were only a few of the old-time stars whose careers began there. The Water Company cannot claim that the scene of the first feature film, "The Great Train Robbery," was in Company territory (it was filmed in Paterson, New Jersey, a few miles away), but the cliffs over which Pearl White was about to be cast at the end of each episode were in the New Jersey Palisades, the country store in the Westerns was probably in Dumont or Tenafly, and the railroad tracks from which the hero rescued the bound and gagged heroine were probably in Teaneck or Leonia. Even this would probably have shocked movie-goers far less than the knowledge that the high stone walls and the great doorway of many baronial English castles in their feature films were the walls and entrance to a crematory in Union Hill.

1917-1949

Shortly after America entered World War I in April, 1917, it became evident to the military authorities that an embarkation camp would be needed near the Hoboken Port of Embarkation if large numbers of American troops were to be shipped to the French front. Having examined and rejected several proposed sites along the Pennsylvania Railroad and the Jersey Central, in middle Jersey, the army turned to a number of sites in Bergen County which had been under consideration two years earlier, at the time of the Vera Cruz incident, when there appeared to be a possibility that troops would have to be sent by ship to Mexico. On July 6, 1917, a group of officers, including Major U. S. Grant III, grandson of President Grant, under the guidance of Mr. Watson G. Clark, a civil engineer of Tenafly, surveyed the sites and conferred with Mr. D. W. French of the Water Company and officials of the New York Central Railroad, the Erie Railroad and the Public Service Electric and Gas Corporation. Two sites were favored, both served by the Hackensack Water Company, one east of Cresskill, the other centered on Madison Avenue and Knickerbocker Road in Dumont. The latter site was chosen, partly because it was largely cleared unimproved land with good drainage, situated on a ridge between the Tenakill and the Long Swamp Brook and served by two railroads, but also because it lay astride one of the main transmission lines of the Water Company. Construction of buildings for several regiments of infantry was started on August 20, 1917, along with various auxiliary buildings, including a 500-bed hospital. Before long troop trains with thousands of khaki-clad soldiers began to arrive on their way to France. The construction of the camp, which was named Camp Merritt, after Major General Wesley Merritt, meant that the Water Company was forced within a few months to add a city of, first, 29,000, and later, 42,000 people to its system, a task which it carried out without the slightest hitch, even though the winter of 1918-1919 was one of the severest on record, and pipes six feet underground were in constant danger of freezing. Nothing now remains of

Camp Merritt, 1918, World War I Embarkation Camp
Courtesy Bergen County Historical Society

the bustling city that once occupied parts of five Bergen County towns but a granite obelisk memorial.

When the war was over, after the short depression of 1921, the Company, like everyone else in America, entered into the euphoria of the 1920's, those golden years when college students in coonskin coats knocked on darkened speakeasy doors and said "Steve sent me"; when stocks rose every day and flappers danced to tunes like Bambalina, Farewell Blues and Way Down Yonder in New Orleans, and Calvin Coolidge's Yankee wisdom cast a warm glow over the whole scene. Suburban houses were going up in Bergen County by the thousands, row on row. Everything was growing and everyone was getting rich.

So far as the Hackensack Water Company was concerned, the only troubler of this Paradise was an aspiring politician from Hoboken, one John J. Fallon, the city's attorney. In 1921 the Company had embarked on an expensive project for enlarging the Oradell Reservoir. Originally the reservoir was nothing but a low dam above Veldran's Mill, with a small mill pond behind it. In 1902, the pond was dredged out and enlarged to provide additional storage, and in 1912 a higher timber-crib dam was built, creating a reservoir which extended several miles back into Emerson. In the 1921 enlargement program, the Company tore out the old timber dam and built a concrete dam of new design, twenty-two feet high, and proceeded to dredge out lands along the river as far back as Harrington Park and Closter, that is to say, the greater part of the present Oradell Reservoir. The enlarged reservoir flooded the junctions of Pascack Creek with the Hackensack River and the junction with the Dwarskill, and raised the water level at Bogert's Mill, on Harriet Avenue, Harrington Park, so that the stream was no longer useful for water power. An extended litigation followed, in which the owners contended unsuccessfully that such a mill could not be condemned for water supply purposes. Sad to say, the new reservoir also obliterated the famous Thirty-foot Hole at the junction of the Dwarskill, which for countless generations had been a favorite swimming place for young people for miles around. The storage in the reservoir was increased to 1,600,000,000 gallons.

If the Company people thought for a moment that a new day had dawned when they completed a reservoir without being denounced as thieves and rascals, they were mistaken. No one

Dredging Oradell Reservoir, c. 1921

rose to denounce the reservoir, but the good people of Hoboken, who had to all appearances been quietly enjoying their beer and busy at their ward politics, were about to enliven things with their own denunciations. At any rate, one of their number, John J. Fallon, was going to enliven things.

Faced with war-time inflation, the expense of reconstructing the reservoir and the criticism of the Board of Public Utilities Commissioners about the low prices for its wholesale sales to Hoboken, which had been consuming a large percentage of its water, the Company decided to file increased tariff rates for Hoboken rather than to seek a general increase of other customers' rates. Mr. Fallon fought this up to the State's highest court and lost. The city, which under the Commission ruling had the alternative of angering its voters by metering its whole system and raising the rates of people who had been paying trifling water bills for years, on the one hand, or installing a city-gate meter and bearing the loss itself, on the other, chose the latter. This proved a mistake, because the water usage shown on the master meter resulted in charges against the city far in excess of the total of its own charges to its customers. The city's leaky system and its careless consumers were wasting large amounts of water, the cost of which had previously been borne by the Water Company, and now would have to be borne by the city.

Mr. Fallon's attacks on the old system having proved disastrous to his client, he soon concluded that the master meter which his officials had demanded was a fire hazard and insisted upon its removal. He also discovered that a part of the Company's oldest building at New Milford had a wooden floor and a few wooden lockers, and complained to the Commission about the "inflammable" construction of the New Milford plant. The Commission approved a Company plan for a sprinkler system in that part of the plant, and brushed off the complaint against the master meter. Moreover, having discovered how leaky the Hoboken system was, the Commission refused to allow the city to revert to the old system of summing up the individual charges, and insisted on charging by the master meter.

Mr. Fallon, in this predicament, understandably turned to alternative sources. A man of somewhat overbearing disposition, John Fallon was regarded by the Water Company as less than a model of civic virtue, and many suspected that the fact that his mentor, Frank Hague, had a water system in Jersey City that badly needed revenue at the time had something to do with the case, but, faced as he was with political realities, even an enemy of Frank Hague could not have refused Jersey City's offer of water at about 60% of the old rate. On November 1, 1923, Hoboken cut itself off the Hackensack system, and the Water Company at one blow lost the revenue from hundreds of thousands of gallons of water a day, for which millions of dollars worth of pipe had been laid and millions of dollars worth of collecting, filtering and pumping capacity had been built. It was a severe economic blow, a blow from which it ultimately recovered, and indeed profited, but one that caused many sleepless nights and in the end brought about a considerable reorganization of the top management. Years later, the Hague organization elevated John J. Fallon to the office of Vice-Chancellor of the State.

At the very peak of the Company's troubles over Hoboken, Bayonne, another Hudson County town, attempted to preempt the Ramapo River in Bergen County as its own source of supply. For some unaccountable reason this led Bergen County's current office-holders to take off after the Water Company, which had been a silent bystander to the intra-county debate, and to threaten a take-over of the Hackensack system. Perhaps they thought that the Company could do something to stop Bayonne if sufficiently scared, though it is hard to see what

Oradell Dam

could have been done. One Bergen County legislator who had been something of a controversial figure in his party and was expecting a stiff primary fight when his term ended, saw the water issue as a godsend, and proceeded to make newspaper headlines by announcing that the Hackensack River watershed was so polluted that it would soon be unfit for use. All water people, public and private, live in dread of such statements, which have often caused near-panics, however ill-founded. Fortunately for the Water Company no one seems to have been taken in by the particular attacks and in due time the voters retired the legislator from office, Bayonne abandoned its Ramapo project, and the whole affair blew over.

By 1926, Mr. Robert deForest had served as President of the Water Company for over forty years. He had seen it grow nearly a thousand-fold under his leadership. He was almost eighty years old, and had been hard at work in recent months finding successors for his posts in the Charity Organization Society, the American Bible Society, the Presbyterian Hospital, the Metropolitan Museum of Art and the Provident Loan Society. He now turned to the task of finding a successor as President of the Water Company. The problem was in one sense an easy one and in other respects extremely difficult. The obvious man for the post was Nicholas S. Hill, Jr., the Company's consulting engineer, a man in his late fifties and a member of the Board of Directors. Two things stood in the way of appointment. Mr. Hill was the head of a successful engineering firm and might not easily be persuaded to take the post, and the appointment of an outsider over the heads of the competent team that had been carrying on operations during Mr. deForest's presidency would obviously be a blow to those men, some of whom had devoted their business lifetimes to the service of the Company. Mr. D. W. French almost certainly regarded himself as the natural successor of Mr. deForest. On the other hand, Mr. Hill and Mr. French had worked closely together on all the

Company's projects for nearly twenty years, and there was every reason to hope that they would continue to work well together, even if Mr. Hill was made President.

Some time during 1926, Mr. Hill agreed to come to the Water Company as its chief executive, and before long the people in the Weehawken office saw that a new office was being set up on the top floor, next to Mr. French's. Some of the more knowledgeable had learned through the grapevine that a new president was coming in, and undoubtedly Mr. French knew who it was, although he was not a man who confided in anyone.

Mr. deForest resigned on March 1, 1926 and Mr. Hill was elected in his place. The change was a milestone in the Company's affairs. Where Mr. French, figuratively at least, had gone to the Board of Directors, hat in hand, for a few thousand dollars of appropriations, Mr. Hill thought in millions. Mr. French, however decisive as the Company's operating executive at Weehawken, had been obliged to listen to the happy thoughts of the Company's directors about this proposal or that; Mr. Hill was an outgoing, thoroughly self-confident man, who was not used to listening to anyone, particularly to those with little knowledge, and he told the Board what he was going to do without waiting for a dissent.

Born in Baltimore in 1869, Nicholas S. Hill had graduated from Stevens Institute of Technology in 1892. After working as a mechanical engineer in Chicago for a few months, he returned to Baltimore, where he was soon promoted to the most important posts in the city's utility departments. He was an able electrical engineer as well as a water engineer, and while at Baltimore designed, among other things, the first large underground electrical conduit system in the United States. Shortly after the turn of the century, he accepted the job of Chief Engineer of New York City's Water Supply and made a considerable name for himself in that position. After a time he resigned to form his own engineering firm, where he established an international reputa-

Nicholas S. Hill
President 1926-1936

tion. He was active in many notable enterprises in the United States, Canada, Cuba, Mexico and China. During World War I, he had been one of the principal engineers who laid out Camp Merritt and several army establishments near Norfolk, Virginia. Latterly, he had become one of the leading figures in the evaluation of public utilities for rate making purposes. He had learned early in his professional career that he could afford to leave technical matters to subordinates, but no one who knew him had any doubt about his technical ability or his ability to get people to do what he wanted them to do. If a group of engineers was hired to do a job, Nicholas S. Hill was the man who wrote the report that went to the top management and the public. Heavy-set, about five feet ten inches tall, he managed by sheer personality to tower over everyone in any meeting.

He had begun to do consulting engineering work for the Water Company in 1910. Mr. Hill had Mr. deForest's talent for finding able assistants, and one of his first moves when he became President of the Water Company was to scour the country for the most competent people he could find. He brought in George Wieghardt, the talented, earnest chief engineer of the Baltimore Water System; he brought in Harrison Cady, a professor at Swarthmore, to improve the pumping station operations; he authorized Charles J. Alfke, who had joined the Water Company three years before, to introduce a modern system of accounting, and he also hired a number of other new men for other tasks. His talent for getting and holding capable men was somewhat curious because there is little evidence that he was particularly interested in people, even able people, once he had found them. George Buck remembers, as a young engineer recently hired by the Hill firm, that Mr. Hill had promised him a $25 a week raise after a few months if his work proved satisfactory. When Mr. Buck came in and reminded him of the promise, Mr. Hill readily ordered the bookkeeper to raise his salary. A few weeks later, however, to Mr. Buck's surprise, he was called into the office and told by Mr. Hill with great solemnity that he had been watching his work and had decided to raise his salary $25 a week. Somewhat stunned at finding that his boss did not remember the earlier visit, but delighted at his unexpected good fortune, he went down and told one of his fellow workers, who was incensed. He said "Damn you, that was my raise you got, not yours," and went up and demanded and got his own $25 raise. When George Buck went back and said he assumed the second raise was a mistake, Mr. Hill told him to forget it, and he kept the two raises.

The election of Mr. Hill was, of course, a great blow to D. W. French, who had spent forty-two years of his life working for the Water Company, most of the time as chief operating executive. His age, of course, was against him, perhaps also the feeling of the directors that the Company had gotten somewhat stodgy in its ways and that a reorganization was needed. Mr. French found himself in a very difficult position. He and Mr. Hill had been good friends, but it was very hard to stand by and see new men replace his own appointees and, perhaps worse to a close-fisted Yankee, to see hundreds of thousands of dollars spent on new projects with less thought than he himself would have given to spending a thousand. When Parliament forced a Whig cabinet on Charles II, he is said to have exclaimed, "God's fish, they have put a set of men about me, but they shall know nothing". It is most unlikely that D. W. French recalled the historic precedent, but he proceeded to act along the same lines. He gave his old employees orders not to help the new men in any way (and was hurt when they failed to carry out his short-sighted directions) and he himself, of course, offered no help. Finally, against the advice of Emile Fricker, one of the few people bold enough to give him any advice, he insisted on writing a long letter to the Board, blasting Mr. Hill's expenditures. The inevitable result was that he found himself with no alternative but to resign. There were few men in the Company who had any reason to regard their self-assured, aloof and demanding former chief executive as a personal friend, but none could fail to see the tragedy of his situation. D. W. French had been responsible for every move the Company had made for nearly forty years. He had come to regard the Company and the Company's employees as his own. There was probably no graceful way for him to leave the center of the stage. If modern retirement plans have no other value than to avoid such situations, they would serve their purpose.

Some time later, Mr. French came by accident upon Mr.

Fricker in a local bank. He came up behind Mr. Fricker, put his hands over Fricker's eyes, and when the latter turned, grasped Fricker's hand warmly and told him that he had been wrong not to follow his advice and tear up the letter to the Board. It was probably one of the few times in D. W. French's life that he had ever conceded that he was wrong about anything.

*   *   *

The boom times of the 20's had brought new problems. As we have seen, the new affluence of working people, born of wartime inflation, made it possible for thousands of Hudson County and New York City people to flee their crowded tenements for the nearby suburbs and rows of development houses soon filled many of the older towns of southern and eastern Bergen County. The demand for water rose year after year. Further development of the Hackensack River source involved the acquisition of thousands of acres of land at what then seemed to be, and indeed were, grossly inflated prices. Nicholas Hill did not hesitate. He set his engineering firm to work on a bold plan to build a high dam at Rivervale and Old Tappan, which would raise the level of the river to seventy-five feet above sea level and flood thousands of acres of land for many miles up into New York State. Mr. Fricker and others were given the task of acquiring the land. The Company's lawyers were directed to apply to the Public Utilities Commission for a rate increase that would make the reservoir financially feasible, and the directors were asked to authorize huge expenditures which would produce no revenues for many years. The commencement of construction of the George Washington Bridge in 1927 emphasized Mr. Hill's wisdom in pressing his plans for additional water resources, for it seemed obvious that the migration to Bergen County's suburbs would be greatly accelerated when the bridge was completed in 1931. Land purchases went along well for a time, despite the fact that every one suspected that the Water Company was buying land for a reservoir and thus had no choice but to pay what was asked for it or risk expensive condemnation proceedings. (Mr. Hill took the pragmatic view that even if people had every reason to suspect that the purchaser was the Water Company, they were not sure unless you told them and insisted on making no announcement, a stand which was probably right.) After a great deal of land had been purchased, the Company's representatives began to find that in one area within the 75-foot flood lines no land could be bought at all, and the local rumor was that it was being bought in dummy names by relatives of one of New York State's most prominent political figures. The first thought, of course, was that if this was true, those well-connected people were planning to hold up the Water Company for a high price. Depressing as that thought was, the actual situation was worse. The buyers had no intention of holding up the Water Company; indeed they probably knew nothing about any proposed reservoir. The charitable view of course would have been that they were merely buying country estates for themselves, but Water Company people have always believed that what the well-connected buyers knew was that the State of New York itself was going to need the land for a large mental hospital at Orangeburg, and that if they could pick up the land at bargain prices from local farmers, the State would soon be paying liberally for it. In due time the Rockland State Hospital was built, and the 75-foot flood line was lost, for there was no way to condemn State Hospital property for a reservoir. The highest possible level was reduced to 55 feet, a loss of about 75% of the planned storage in the reservoir. As it turned out, a lot of water was to flow down the river before the Company felt the effect of the loss, the flows of forty years, as a matter of fact. The Company was to have many other things to worry about before it felt the loss of twenty feet of reservoir elevation.

* * *

In writing of the Company's troubles, it would be easy to pass over an important technical development in water purification for which the Hackensack Water Company takes credit, or to be more exact, credits its distinguished Sanitary Engineer, Mr. George Spalding. In the latter years of the 1920's, Mr. Spalding conceived an idea for dealing with a problem that had plagued the waterworks industry for years, the problem of finding a method of using activated carbon in water treatment. Activated carbon had long been recognized as an efficient means of removing tastes and odors in other cases, and many efforts had been made to apply the techniques to water supply systems. All of these had been disappointing. The most promising proposal was to substitute activated carbon for the sand in filter beds, but the light-weight carbon simply did not lend itself to the purpose, and even when it was used it produced little improvement in taste or odor. Mr. Spalding proposed a radically different method of using the carbon. Instead of placing it in a filter bed, he suggested that if it were applied in a finely powdered form prior to coagulation, where the carbon could do the job it was intended to do and nothing else, the sand filters could continue to do their separate jobs. He set Paul Tamer, the Company's Chief Chemist, to work on experiments with powdered carbon along these lines, and the results were so encouraging that they were reported in a paper presented at the New York meeting of the American Water Works Association on May 2, 1929.

There was, however, considerable scepticism. Many experienced water experts doubted whether the small quantity of powder which Mr. Spalding and Mr. Tamer proposed to use would have any real effect, and others feared that the minute carbon particles would pass through the treatment process into the distribution system. Mr. Spalding's tests indicated that even small quantities applied by his method would greatly improve tastes and odors and that none of the carbon would pass into the system, almost all of the particles being removed in coagulation and the balance being trapped in the filters. A month-long experiment with the whole water system was made in March, 1930, at the New Milford plant, during a time when water organisms were particularly prevalent, with startling effects. In actual practice, half the quantity of carbon used in the laboratory was fully effective, and none whatever passed through the filters. In

Dinner for Mr. George Spalding
on His Retirement in 1949

March, 1931, the Company decided to use the process on a continuous basis. It is now standard in water systems throughout the world. Mr. Spalding modestly described his process as "nothing but a simple and surprisingly effective method" of applying activated carbon. In fact it was his discovery that made activated carbon useful in providing pure and palatable water, a discovery so highly regarded by the waterworks industry that he was later given the George W. Fuller Memorial Award of the American Water Works Association.

*   *   *

In the latter years of the twenties the country had been in the middle of the most inflationary period it had ever experienced. Elevator operators, college students, store clerks and everyone else was buying stocks on thin margins, and many had amassed large paper fortunes by doing so. The *Times* stock index, which had stood at 106 in May, 1924, reached 181 at the end of 1925, 245 at the end of 1927, 331 at the end of 1928, and 449 at the end of August, 1929, an increase of 400%. (During the same period industrial production had risen no more than 20%.) Glamor issues of new and promising enterprises rose several points every day and many otherwise sober investors, who had watched Radio Corporation of America, for example, a "growth stock" of the day, though no one had yet invented the term, rise from 85 to 420 (adjusted for comparison) from January to December, 1928, though it had never paid a dividend, were certain that a new era had dawned and that it would be worth 1,000 within a few months. (It reached a low of 10 a few years later.) Just as Dutchmen who paid $30,000 for a single tulip bulb during Holland's tulip mania in the 1600's had no thought of planting the bulb, no one cared whether Radio paid a dividend or not. The only value of property ownership became the prospect of an early rise in its price. Brokers' loans, the best index of margin buying, rose from a normal billion and a half to more than seven billion dollars by the fall of 1929. As in the 1870's the actual number of stock speculators was small—no more than 1,500,000 in the whole country at the height of the 1929 speculation — but it would have been hard to find anyone in the country who was not in greater or less degree bound up in the boom. In some ways, it had become central to American culture, and the same easy and careless attitude that had marked the post-Civil War period was repeated in exaggerated form.

*   *   *

Automobiles had changed people's lives far more than stock speculation. No longer the playthings of the rich, tens of thousands of them poured out of New York City over the ferries into New Jersey every Sunday morning, to be joined by thousands of others from the suburbs, and from sundown to midnight thousands stood in long lines, often reaching miles back from the ferry slips at Weehawken, Edgewater, Englewood Cliffs and Alpine, waiting to return home. Bergen County's roads were filled. In fact there were some figures which suggested that the County held more cars for its population than any in the nation, which had nine million automobiles on the road in 1920. Five years later there were more than twice as many, and by 1930 there were more than twenty-six million. So many motorists were essaying long trips in the early 1920's that someone with a flair for such things conceived of a highway to run from the Atlantic to the Pacific, to be called the Lincoln Highway, which a driver could follow without stopping for directions and without consulting his Blue Book to tell whether to take the right or the left fork at the red school house. He devised the simple but ingenious system of painting a set of red, white and blue stripes around telephone poles, trees and posts along the way, and before long someone else improved upon the idea by giving numbers to through automobile routes and painting the numbers on poles and trees.

Numbered highways were only one of many things we now take for granted which were startling novelties when they first appeared in the twenties. Red and green lights which directed traffic without a police officer were tried at a few places and quickly spread over the nation. One-way streets were introduced. A number of homes along main highways put out signs reading "Tourists Welcome", and when these began to flourish, someone else conceived the idea of building tourist cabins, which soon became even more popular, the forerunners of the modern motel.

Where baseball and boxing had once been the concern of adolescents and a none-too-highly regarded "sporting element", baseball, boxing, football, tennis and golf became almost universal spectator (or better, listener and reader) sports, with names like Jack Dempsey, Babe Ruth, Bobby Jones, Bill Tilden, Glenna Collett, Helen Wills and Red Grange on every tongue. The whole character of advertising changed to its modern form. Two young college graduates, with the not uncommon New York City surnames of Simon and Schuster, went into the advertising business to promote a new car called the Jordan Playboy. They wasted no advertising space on horsepower, performance, price or workmanship, and little on the appearance of their product, focussing instead on the beautiful girls and the good life that possession of a Jordan car promised to its fortunate owner, making explicit the dream of every red-blooded young American that nothing but the ownership of a Stutz Bearcat, a Mercer Roadster or a Wills-St. Claire stood between him and his fondest hopes of Paradise, and in Englewood, Ridgewood and Hackensack, clean-cut young men in Brooks suits and tanned young girls in polo coats seemed to be living proof of the dream as they rode by on their way to the Field Club or the Country Club in their expensive cars.

America had passed over a great divide in 1919, when, for the first time in history, there was no longer a fundamental shortage of goods, but a surplus, and Americans, rich and poor alike, were revelling in the new-found freedom that such a world brought.

The middle class, perhaps most evidently in places like the

Bergen County suburbs, were beginning to taste some of the pleasures of affluence hitherto reserved for the rich. Country clubs were filled and new clubs built. Solid Bergen County people of the kind who would have been found at Wednesday prayer meetings ten or twenty years before, now more often spent their evenings at the theater, and many Jersey Dutchmen whose parents had supped on mush and milk thought it incumbent upon themselves to adopt, or to affect to adopt, the public morals of the idle rich and the shiftless poor. The fast set of Bergen County and northern Hudson spent Saturday evenings dining and dancing at the local "road houses", the suburban counterparts of city speakeasies, Allendale Inn, the Bluebird at Cedar Lane and Teaneck Road in Teaneck, the Arcola Manor, or the Villa Richard in Fort Lee, to name a few, the latter reputed to be particularly sophisticated. People who made it their business to know such things whispered from time to time that this or that well-known County figure had been caught in a raid at some such place under compromising circumstances. Americans of the twenties who were not involved in public drinking, sports cars, hip flasks, college football, the theater, foreign travel, hot jazz, coonskin coats, short dresses and loose morals felt very much out of things, though few actually lived up to this popular image of good living. What passed for sophistication was the order of the day: Vanity Fair, H. L. Mencken and George Jean Nathan vied with each other, and with hundreds of imitators, to put an end to America's Bible Belt morality, offering their own immature hedonism as the *summum bonum* of the ages.

Public relations came into its own: John D. Rockefeller, under the tutelage of Ivy Lee, made headlines by handing out a dime now and then at strategic places. Others needed no professional advice about self-promotion. Small-bore literati, whose works are long since forgotten, puffed up the reputations of others with no more talent than their own; lunch-time insults at a

corner table at the Algonquin Hotel on 44th Street, little different from those of the construction workers on the new Para-
mount Building down the street but regularly reported in the
smart journals of the day, built up national reputations for wit.
Show business people, who would have been refused admittance
at the Tradesman's Entrance of a respectable business man's
home a few years before, were wined and dined like royalty.
The gay lives of movie stars and café society figures became
the meat and drink of readers of the new tabloid papers, which
made no pretense that they were interested in anything but
scandal, sports and crime. Radio brought popular entertainment
into the living room, and millions who had never entered a
vaudeville theater now sagely compared the routines of Eddie
Cantor, George Burns and Gracie Allen, and the Two Black
Crows.* Between 7:00 and 7:15 o'clock every weekday night,
Amos and Andy held the nation enthralled with the machina-
tions of the Kingfish against their pure and simple heroes. A

---

* The people who lived near the Company's Weehawken office may
have been somewhat more sophisticated. Samuel W. Zerman, who lived
in Weehawken at the time, remembers when many of the famous vaudeville stars, including George Burns, Gracie Allen and Eddie Cantor
during their early careers, performed regularly at the celebrated Hudson
Theater, which stood a few blocks west of the office. At one time the
theater had stock company performances during the week and vaudeville on Sunday nights, when the New York theaters were closed.
"Uncle Tom's Cabin" was an annual stock company production. With
the decline of vaudeville and stock company theaters, the Hudson became one of the few burlesque theaters in the New York area. The
Hudson Dispatch, a leading newspaper in Hudson County, had its offices
opposite the theater. Its owner, Thomas F. Martin, was a colorful political figure who resided in Weehawken and was at one time Secretary of State of New Jersey. He was particularly offended by the
raffish crowd who attended the performances and the frequent collisions
with the police, and finally, strongly supported by the nearby St. Augus-
tine's Roman Catholic Church and the Baptist Church, he was able to
close the theater. In the 1910 era the Lyric Theater in Hackensack also
had stock company performances and vaudeville.

young man no one had ever heard of went out to a Long Island airfield one day and set off without fanfare in a little plane hardly bigger than a good-sized automobile and landed in Paris thirty-three hours later. Charles Lindbergh came back to these shores in an American warship to be greeted by a Broadway welcoming parade hardly equalled since.

We know now that it was like a huge champagne party on a ship racing to its destruction, but in truth most of the exuberance of the twenties was innocuous enough, and, except for the stock market speculation, probably had nothing to do with the holocaust to come.

So far as the Water Company was concerned, except that all of its people were caught up in the times, the principal effect of the boom was the tremendous expansion of real estate development that brought to Bergen County tens of thousands of new people who had never before been able to own their own homes. The population rose 73% between 1920 and 1930. Farms were broken up into building lots and thousands of new houses soon filled the new streets. The collapse of the Florida boom in 1926, instead of slowing down the Bergen County boom, brought dozens of high pressure real estate operators into the County, where they hoped that the new George Washington Bridge would enable them to recoup their recent losses in the south. Teaneck had been a town of farmlands, with perhaps a dozen thinly built-up roads. It became a huge suburban city almost overnight. Every new house meant more demand for water. As we have seen, the Water Company had already committed itself to building a new reservoir at Rivervale to meet these demands. It also laid thousands of feet of pipe and thousands of services in newly-paved streets in advance of development trying to keep up with the boom.

*　　*　　*

By the fall of 1929 there were enough signs of nervousness in the stock market (which had fallen back sharply on September 3rd, and less sharply during the rest of September and early October) so that a certain number of professional stock speculators, notably (at least by reputation) Jesse L. Livermore, felt that there was an opportunity to make profitable short sales, and on October 20, 21 and 22, the *New York Times* reported, a powerful bear pool operating in Wall Street drove stocks down ten or twenty points. As always, market analysts came forward to announce, with equal solemnity and assurance, on the one hand, that even at current high levels, prices were not up to true value, and, on the other, that further lows were in prospect.

In the 1873 Panic, few of the people of Hackensack had any direct concern with Wall Street, which was an arcane world of rich and powerful men, far removed from the daily life of Bergen County farmers. In 1929, however, there were few in Bergen County and northern Hudson County who did not in one degree or another have some connection with the world of banking and finance, if only because many of their good friends and neighbors worked in the Street. Towns like Englewood were little more than bedrooms for the well-to-do of Wall Street. The total number of Bergen County people with brokerage accounts could not have been great, but it represented a far higher percentage of the population than in most places, and virtually everyone followed the market, whether he had a financial stake in it or not.

The losses on October 20, 21 and 22 had shaken the market. October 23 was worse, with four billions lost in a day's trading, most of it in the last hour. The next day, October 24th, Black Thursday, started the Panic of 1929. Nearly 13,000,000 shares were sold in a day of fright, disorder and confusion, as wave after wave of distress selling hit the market. A coalition of New York's leading bankers was formed to try to stem the selling tide, and it did reverse the trend by noon of that day, but the damage had already been done. By the 28th, the bankers were

New York Times, October 30, 1929

forced to give up when it became clear that no one group could stem the torrent of sales, and a further drop of ten billion dollars occurred. At times there were no bids at all for important stocks. Sales by Europeans and country banks added to the liquidation, and each sale of securities by over-extended speculators set off a chain reaction of new sales. Since there were only about seven billion dollars of margin loans, and the losses to date far exceeded that figure, it was not only margin accounts that were now driving the market down, but liquidation by wealthy investors forced to sell. On October 29, the final crash came. The market suffered the most disastrous day in Wall Street's history, and the headlines the next morning read: "Stocks Collapse in 16,410,030-Share Day:"

"Stock prices virtually collapsed yesterday, swept downward with gigantic losses in the most disastrous trading day in the stock market's history, [the story began]. . . . Hysteria swept the country and stocks went overboard for just what they would bring at forced sale. . . .

"Banking support, which would have been impressive and successful under ordinary circumstances, was swept violently aside, as block after block of stocks . . . deluged the market. . . . Quotations plunged downward in a day of disorganization, confusion and financial impotence." *(The New York Times, October 30, 1929.)*

Crowds milled about Broad Street and Wall Street. Jimmy Walker urged movie exhibitors not to show gloomy newsreels of the disaster. A few days later, John D. Rockefeller made his famous statement that "My son and I are buying common stocks," but nothing could stop the waves of liquidation, which produced another drop of five to sixty-six points on November 5th. By now, no one was talking any longer of a "new era" in finance. Leading bankers tried to allay the panic by announcements that the reaction had overrun itself. Politicians, never at a loss to explain any disaster while there are opposing politicians to blame, were clear, on one side, that the crash had come because the Hoover administration's tariff bill was threatened with defeat, and on the other, that the administration had brought economic disaster. Prominent market operators were readily available as whipping boys for populist Senators; clergymen felt that "financiers" were morally obligated to refund speculators' losses. (It is somewhat startling to read that John J. Raskob was attacked for saying before the crash that General Motors was worth twelve times earnings, hardly a price-earnings ratio to worry an investor forty years later.) The Exchange itself tried to discourage short selling. The Treasury was certain that the break was due to speculation and not to any basic business weakness. One pundit took comfort from the fact that the country had suffered many billions of dollars of paper losses "without serious harm to the average person." Senator Capper, who had made a place for himself as a spokesman for the farmer, said that farmers were not excited about the crash, and even J. P. Morgan, who had been prudently silent for weeks, finally said that the worst was over. The *London Economist* felt that the crash would aid the economy by diverting funds from speculation.

Sad to say, all of them were wrong. The worst was not yet over; farmers were to suffer more from the debacle than stock market speculators; the average person was to suffer unimaginable harm from the crash; the economy was not aided by the crash, it was virtually destroyed. As in 1873, observers may have been quite right in saying that the crash was due to speculation and not to basic business weakness, but, also as in 1873, the stock market crash destroyed the credit and confidence on which all business was conducted, and business could not have suffered a greater disaster if it had been rotten to the core.

President Hoover assured the country that its fundamental economics were sound, that only speculative business had been destroyed, but the panic continued. Margin clerks toiled through the night for months at a time calling margin loans to be dumped on the market the next morning, and the market continued to fall. Creditors rushed in to collect their debts before business declined further and closed the doors of many concerns that might have survived. Before long even many solid businesses were in danger of bankruptcy. The Water Company was in no such danger; indeed it proved to be one of the most stable enterprises whose securities were listed on the New York Stock Exchange, but even Water Company officials, who had assumed that people would buy water whether or not the boom collapsed, now found that many industrial users were no longer buying anything at all, and that even private customers found it possible to cut down sharply on the amount they used. Many houses, of course, were vacated, as mortgages were foreclosed, and families moved in together. New construction stopped entirely. Within a year or two water use again reached 1929 levels, but the halcyon days of expansion seemed to have ended forever. The last thing in the world the Water Company needed at the moment was a new reservoir. Its problem was to get the capital to pay off the debts it had incurred to buy the land and finance the expansion that the boom had forced on it. By 1931, the Company, which had never theretofore had the least difficulty in borrowing money, was obliged to pledge $1,500 of bonds for each $1,000 it borrowed, and to pay 7% for the money even with such collateral. Even the completion of the George Washington Bridge linking Bergen County with Manhattan in 1931 had little effect on the Company's business at the time, however-much it filled the County's roads with automobiles, and however disastrous its effects upon the railroad commuting lines and the trolleys. It was 1946 before the full impact of the Bridge began to be felt.

*   *   *

In 1931, Henry L. deForest was made Chairman of the Board of the Company, with Mr. Hill continuing as President and chief executive officer. Mr. deForest had been a director for twenty years and, through his father and his law firm, represented a link to the very beginnings of the modern Hackensack Water Company. Henry deForest was one of the most kindly, cheerful and friendly men who ever lived. Slightly deaf, he never allowed his handicap to embitter him or to make him suspicious of others, and no one could possibly have been more unselfishly dedicated to the business of bringing pure water to the people of northeastern New Jersey. He was utterly unable to conceive of any compromise in the high standards which his father had set for the Company; in point of fact his uncompromising attitude may at times have been somewhat frustrating to men who had to deal with the work-a-day problems of relations with demanding

Henry L. deForest,
Chairman of the Board 1931-1936. President 1936-1950

public officials, avaricious contractors, crotchety employees and captious customers.

In 1936, Mr. Hill died, at the age of 67. His death was a great blow to the Company, for it was obvious to all that it would be impossible to find a man of his wide experience and great executive ability to take his place. None existed. It was decided not to go out of the Company for a new chief executive, but to name Mr. Henry deForest as President and Mr. Charles J. Alfke as a Vice President and manager of the Company's affairs, an arrangement reminiscent of the years in which Mr. deForest's father was President and Mr. D. W. French was Superintendent in charge of active operations. At the bottom of the depression of the 1930's, with little or no expansion, the arrangement worked quite well. Mr. deForest limited his activities largely to matters of broad policy, and Mr. Alfke dealt with the other business of the Company.

The depression which followed the 1929 crash lasted twelve years, and might have lasted to this day but for the artificial stimulus of a great world war. For more than a decade, politicians made great capital of the public distrust of business engendered by the crash, and business, for its part, suspicious of politicians, seemed to oppose even the most necessary measures to ease the distress of the victims of depression. The whole fabric of American society was torn asunder by mutual distrust, a distrust that is by no means dissipated a quarter of a century later. It has been estimated that, by 1932, industry was operating at one-half of its 1929 level, and that the major businesses of the country were suffering combined losses of $5,000,000,000 a year. No one could possibly estimate the annual losses of small businesses; the only thing that could be said with certainty was that a large percentage of them were not operating at all. Bergen County's real estate boom, which had shown signs of weakness before 1929, was but a faint memory, revived as one passed mile after mile of sidewalks and paved roads overgrown with weeds and brush. Stores which were not wholly vacated were almost empty. No one thought of buying stocks or bonds, people were far too concerned over their own tax sales and mortgage foreclosures. No Water Company people lost their jobs, but even people fortunate enough to hold on to their own jobs could not fail to despair at the tragedies around them, at relatives and neighbors, once prosperous, reduced to living on relief or on their relatives' charity or even more tragically by selling off their possessions at distress prices. Silver tea sets were sold for less than their value as metal; irreplaceable antique furniture was sold at junkyard prices. Worst of all were the tragedies of blasted careers, energetic, ambitious young men in Bergen and northern Hudson Counties, many with brilliant college records, who had been at the very threshold of success in Wall Street, in advertising or in merchandizing, were working on WPA projects or at clerks' jobs. There had been many stock market panics before. The 1873 crash had brought business to its knees, but in each of them things began to move again after a time. As years went on, the 1929 depression seemed to have become a permanent way of life, the more tragic because all too many of its victims had come to accept their misfortunes as beyond remedy.

The genius of America for centuries was that men were both wanted and needed, and that they were rewarded—albeit not with universal justice—for their ability to contribute to society's needs. Now America was little different from the despairing England that the great puritan John Winthrop described in 1629:

> "This lande grows wearye of her Inhabitantes, so as man which is the most pretious of all the Creatures, is here more vile, and base, than the earthe they treade upon; so as children, neighbours, and friends (especially if they be poore) are rated the greatest burdens, which if things were right would be the cheifest earthly blessings."

Men were indeed rated as burdens. It was a tragic era, which has affected the life of every American who has lived since, and will continue to affect Americans as long as its tragedies are remembered.

* * *

On December 4, 1941, the Company entered into the first contract with the Utility Workers Union of America, CIO, the union which had been chosen by Company employees as their bargaining agent after considerable controversy. Labor negotiations have been in the capable hands of Vice President Julius Von Scheidt for most of the time since that date.

At the beginning of World War II, some of the older men in the Company were reminded of the days of World War I, for the Army again found the Hackensack Valley the logical site

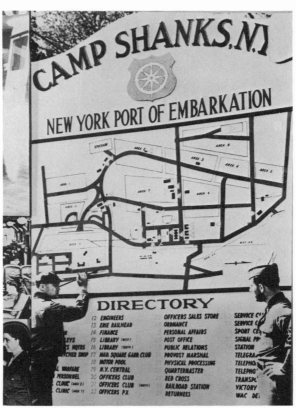

Camp Shanks, World War II Embarkation Camp
Courtesy Tappan Zee Historical Society

Charles J. Alfke,
Vice President
and Manager; later
Executive Vice President
1936-1958

for a major embarkation camp. The old Camp Merritt site was by now filled with houses. Orangeburg, in Rockland County, was chosen as the site of Camp Shanks. Like Camp Merritt, it was a huge city of wooden barracks built almost overnight, and with even heavier demands for water. The Hackensack Water Company brought its mains to the state line (the Spring Valley system, which was also furnishing large quantities of water, could not have supplied the huge amounts that were needed from its underground sources), and the Army took the Hackensack water over the state line into Camp Shanks, a transfer which would have been prohibited by state law if the Water Company had undertaken to do so itself. (The laws of both New York and New Jersey now wisely permit such transfers if authorized by the appropriate authorities.) Despite wartime shortages of both men and materials, Charles Alfke and the other operating officials of the Company maintained its services without the

EXECUTIVE STAFF, 1949

Seated L. to R.: John C. Schlicht, Earle Talbot, George Spalding, Henry L. deForest, Charles J. Alfke, Emile J. Fricker. *Seated Second Row, L. to R.:* Joseph Domas, Victor Aldoretta, Thomas Adams, Anthony Zoeller, Lawrence Hogan. *Third Row, L. to R.:* Adolph Damiano, Archibald Lyle, Thomas Mitchell, Wesley Gutteridge, Peter Pallo, M. Warren Cowles, Harrison Cady, Adrian C. Leiby, George MacCoubrey, John N. Miraglia, Joseph Liccardi, Samuel W. Zerman, George J. Schmidle, George Cavanaugh, Arnold Staub, John W. Lipinski. *Fourth Row, L. to R.:* Edward Walasyk, Walter Brown, Walter H. Boquist, Charles Jost (Buck, Seifert & Jost, Consulting Engineers), Julius Von Scheidt, William Block, Henry Hein, George F. Wieghardt.

slightest interruption throughout the whole period of the war.

In 1946, the Company was able to sell its Thirty-year First Mortgage Bonds at an effective interest rate of less than 2.40%, either the lowest or next-to-the-lowest rate ever paid by a utility company for such funds.

Few Americans can bring themselves to remember, in light of later events, that they believed when the war ended that the country would go back to the depression levels that prevailed before the war, and that the small boom that followed V-J Day was but a prelude to a collapse of business. The end of war spending and the return of millions of men to a work force which already far exceeded in numbers the pre-war work force of the country seemed certain to bring on a disaster. Office-seekers—those sure barometers of public concern—sought votes by little else but assurances that if elected they would keep people at work and warnings that if their particular programs for spending billions were not adopted the country was headed for a new depression. Nor were business leaders any more omniscient than office-seekers: Sewell Avery of Montgomery Ward was by no means the only business man who was carefully nursing his war-time savings to carry him through the coming depression. In truth, most knowledgeable people half feared that the pessimists were right, and shook their heads in amazement at those few who were bold enough to predict a great business boom.

New house construction in the Company's service area had virtually ended when the Bergen County real estate boom collapsed in 1929, almost twenty years before. Most people in the area had been busy ever since trying to pay off the public debt that the local politicians and the road contractors had burdened them with at the height of the boom. A good part of Bergen County's vacant land was held by municipalities for unpaid taxes. The Water Company had easily kept up with the modest increases in demand by utilizing the water sources developed in the

1920's and by purchasing water from nearby systems. If new house construction went back to pre-war levels, water supply seemed to present no problems whatever. Even if construction went to higher levels, the Company still had a margin of safe yield over anticipated demands and it had neighboring systems which were happy to sell water at wholesale. If worst came to worst, it owned most of the land needed to build a reservoir to a 55 foot elevation at Rivervale. No one supposed that any such problem would arise.

1950-1969

It is something of an oversimplification to say that the people of Rockland County, Bergen County and northern Hudson County are indebted to one man for a substantial fraction of the water they use, but there is good reason to believe that 20,000,000 gallons a day from the Hackensack River would have been lost to public use if George Wieghardt, a blunt water engineer with no interest whatever in public acclaim, had not moved to save it when he did.

As has been said, when Nicholas Hill was named President, he brought Mr. Wieghardt (who had been in charge of the Baltimore water system when Mr. Hill was its consulting engineer) to the Company, taking advantage of the fact that Mr. Wieghardt had found himself temporarily out of a job when a new group of politicians came into power in Baltimore. George Wieghardt may have been something of a trial to his former employers, for he made no effort whatever to hide his low regard for politicians; indeed, for anyone who got along by winning friends and influencing people, a group in which he generally lumped everyone but civil engineers. Once he had made an engineering decision, he wasted no time in pondering the intangible considerations affecting the case. Many of his fellow officials suspected that he had an ability to turn off his own sense of hearing after announcing a decision. He prided himself on his bluntness, and won considerable wry admiration for it.

No one doubted that he was wholly dedicated to the task of providing pure water for the people of Bergen, Hudson and Rockland Counties; in point of fact, he had a one-track mind on the subject.

For a number of years, no one knows how many, George Wieghardt had spent many of his Sundays and other spare time studying additional reservoir sites on the Hackensack River. One such site stood out over all the alternatives. North of Mill Road in Clarkstown there was a long narrow swamp, almost uninhabited except for a few houses in low areas, indeed virtually uninhabitable without extensive drainage and filling, if at all. High hills rose up on both sides of the swamp, so that a comparatively short dam at the southern end would create a deep narrow lake about four and a half miles long with virtually no road crossings. It was an ideal place for a reservoir.

The location was not unknown as a possible reservoir site; it had been a part of the 75 foot elevation reservoir designed by Nicholas Hill two decades earlier, a part of the reservoir which was lost when plans had to be cut back to a 55 foot elevation, but no one else in the Company had given it any active thought for years, if indeed it had ever been seriously considered as a separate reservoir at the 85 foot elevation now contemplated. What Mr. Wieghardt brought to the case was the realization, first, that the time was fast approaching when two additional reservoirs, not one, would be needed to supply the growing population of northeast New Jersey and Rockland County, New York, and, second, that under the present circumstances the Clarkstown site ought to be developed before the long planned Rivervale site. The second point was only in a minor degree technical. What Mr. Wieghardt saw was that the project he had been thinking about for years was now threatened by plans for a Tappan Zee Bridge, a New York Thruway and a Palisades Interstate Parkway; that Rockland County would soon repeat the Bergen County building boom which was already in progress, and that, if experience in Bergen County was any guide, a money hungry developer would just as soon build his houses on drained swampland as anywhere else if the price was right. Such a turn of events would quickly destroy the only remaining reservoir site on the river, a water source sufficient to supply 200,000 people for centuries. Obvious as the situation was, it was one that would only have occurred to a dedicated water man, one who has been conditioned by experience to know that water supplies must be planned in terms of centuries, not in terms of years. In candor, not all dedicated water men would have pushed the idea. It required a man who could be deaf to a multitude of reasonable objections to the project. George Wieghardt was not interested in objections, nor in waiting for a favorable opportunity to win people over to his views; he was interested in a northern reservoir and the 20,000,000 gallons of water a day which was going to be lost if people listened to objections. To most business men, it would be utter folly to spend millions of dollars for land to build a new reservoir in New York when the Company already had millions of dollars invested in a reservoir site in New Jersey which was not being used, particularly when the Company had for years received no return on its investment in the land held for future reservoir use. To others, the fact that the site was in New York State, out of the service area of the Hackensack Water Company, would have ruled it out, for it required no great imagination to see what regulatory troubles might ensue on both sides of the State line from such a situation.

When George Wieghardt saw, or believed he saw, that ordinary channels had failed to get his project accepted, he bundled up his papers and plans and went over to see Henry L. deForest in New York City. Mr. deForest was no great crony of George Wieghardt. He had probably had little personal contact with him before he submitted the northern reservoir project, but Mr. deForest's very lack of contact with the day-to-day

George F. Wieghardt
Chief Engineer 1938-1954

workings of the Company, a matter that probably gave him some concern, made him the more receptive to a project where an executive decision at the highest level was indicated. In any case, he assured Mr. Wieghardt that he was interested, and proceeded to bring the subject to the attention of the Administrative Committee of the two companies on a confidential basis. Earlier legal studies of the feasibility of an interstate project were reexamined in detail as they applied to the particular reservoir and the involved questions of the inter-company relations between Spring Valley, which would build any reservoir, and the Hackensack Water Company, which would have to finance it in its early years, were brought forward for study. Mr. deForest called in the Company's consulting engineers, Messrs. Buck, Seifert and Jost, to review the feasibility of the project, to study the long-term water requirements of Rockland County and the Hackensack service area, the probable cost, and other engineering problems.

To anyone who saw the situation in perspective, the case for building the northern reservoir could not have been simpler. The Clarkstown Reservoir would add about 20,000,000 gallons a day of "safe yield"; that is, enough water to supply about 200,000 people in the Hackensack Valley. If the reservoir site was lost to real estate developers, water for those 200,000 people would be lost forever.

Mr. C. Earl Morrow, consultant to the Regional Plan Association and the Rockland County Planning Board, and even more recently to the Town of Clarkstown, where the reservoir was to be located, put the matter in a nutshell in a radio talk made a year or so later, after the project was publicly announced. (Unknown to the Company until after it had made its own plans, Mr. Morrow had himself proposed that the site be used as a reservoir.) He pointed out that a reservoir in the area would soon be a compelling necessity, and went on to say:

"As to the site, I believe it is the best one for the purpose. . . . [It] is adaptable through the construction of a relatively short dam; the land covered is not suitable for buildings; the enhancement of the surrounding area would be considerable. . . . It seems to me that now is the time to construct the reservoir. Although the land is not suitable for buildings, that doesn't mean that some people will not try to establish homes there. I can show you areas in the region where a [small] rainfall will flood lawns and cellars. . . . The area is a potential liability in view of the development that would be attempted if the lake is not created."

This, of course, was exactly the point that George Wieghardt was making. The reservoir was a compelling necessity and had to be built at once to forestall unwise development. He was too polite, or perhaps too discreet, to comment on the complications which business men, financial people and lawyers began to inject into the case. Whether it came to his mind or not, there is every reason to suppose that Daniel Defoe's picture of Gulliver—an engineer—pinned to the ground by hundreds of

Lilliputians—lawyers, accountants and public officials—described his view of himself as well as anything. In an engineer's Paradise, the reservoir would have been built at once; in the real world there are matters of money and people and governments to deal with. Fortunately for his sanity, at about this time he returned to the heavy load of his regular engineering work, and left the principal worries of the reservoir to others. It is well that he did; the events of the next few years would have been trying indeed for anyone who saw the importance of the end result and had no patience with details. Of course there were details, multitudes of them. There was the matter of money. Spring Valley would have to build the reservoir, but in the early years it had no use for the water and accordingly could provide no revenues to build or carry such a multi-million dollar project. The logic of the case was again simple enough; if Spring Valley was to preserve the water that it would require in later years, the only way to do so was to get Hackensack, the downstream owner, to advance the money and pay the carrying charges in the intervening period, with Spring Valley reserving the right to take and pay for its share of the water when it needed it. Hackensack needed the additional "safe yield" at once, and could and should pay most of the cost until Spring Valley began to use the water. The problem was by no means academic. It was not a case of transferring money from one pocket to the other, because the impact of the costs would fall on the rate-payers in two different states, who were subject to two different rate-making authorities; indeed, the fear that the two companies would be whipsawed between the two states, with each state claiming that the ratepayers of the other should bear the full cost, was a spectre that haunted the project from the outset. The concept of a proper inter-company contract was relatively simple: the downstream owner, Hackensack, would say to the upstream owner, Spring Valley, "If you build a regulating reservoir, I will lend you the money to build it and you can pay me out of my part of the regulating charges. We will divide the cost between us on the basis of the current benefits of regulation. I will pay most of the costs now; when you begin to need the water, you will pay your share, based upon the amount you draw." The detailed contract, of course, had to be far more complicated, and was subject to review by regulatory authorities of two states, no simple matter in itself. Nor is the acquisition of land for a reservoir a simple process, since the buyer can never say "Your price is exorbitant. I will buy elsewhere." Neither are detailed engineering plans or construction contracts simple things.

In May, 1950, in the early stages of planning the reservoir, but after it had been definitely determined to proceed, Mr. Henry L. deForest decided to step down as active head of the Company. He was seventy-five years old at the time and had served as chief executive officer during the past fourteen years. It is unlikely that the reservoir project had much to do with his decision to move from the Presidency to the office of Chairman of the Board, but in retrospect the decision was fortunate, for a kindly old gentleman of a past age, full of the milk of human kindness, would have been distressed indeed to find himself in the front line of the unpleasant controversy that soon developed. To find a new president, Mr. deForest and the Board turned to the same place that the Company had turned twenty years before, the old engineering firm of Nicholas S. Hill, Jr., in point of fact, to Mr. Hill's successor as head of the firm, Mr. George H. Buck. George Buck had graduated from the engineering school of the University of Pennsylvania in 1918, and after working on the water supplies of Athens and Piraeus, Greece, joined the Nicholas Hill organization, which he headed in 1950. Like Mr. Hill, he had won an international reputation in his field and was currently engaged as consulting engineer for a number of water supply studies and development projects in the West Indies and South America, as well as many domestic projects. The Company was fortunate indeed to be able to persuade him to add the duties of chief executive to his busy professional obligations. Mr. Buck had worked with the Hackensack Water Company for more than a quarter of a century as a consulting engineer, and had been actively involved in all of its other problems during that time. He was already well acquainted with most of the people at the Company.

What he did not know, and no one else knew, was that he was stepping into a controversy in which his very election as President was to be attacked as a scheme to hire a polished witness to hide the sinister plans of the Company, and his simplest statements of engineering facts were to be attacked as paid fabrications.

On February 1, 1951, a public statement was made about the plans for the Clarkstown Reservoir. This was followed promptly by talks to many local organizations, at which those present were encouraged to ask any questions that came to mind about the project. The talks were so frequent that George Buck must have wondered whether he had been hired as a luncheon speaker or a corporate executive. The influential local newspaper greeted the plan as a useful public improvement. Land acquisitions seemed to go forward with no more than ordinary trouble. The companies' representatives made every effort to assure people in the vicinity that a bare minimum of houses would be taken. Most of the houses in the area were along the roads on top of the hills bordering the site, houses that, as time has proved, stood to benefit greatly by having a lake rather than a swamp in back of them. A few unfortunately were in locations where they could not be saved, but there was good reason to believe that all but a few of the owners of those houses were prepared to sell for a price and move to a more desirable location elsewhere.

Within two months after the announcement, a few rumblings of controversy turned into a campaign of abuse of the water companies that made the Woodcliff Lake dispute, to borrow

George H. Buck,
President 1950-
Fred Van Dyke

Garret Ackerson's old phrase, look like a Quaker meeting. Without support from the Rockland *Journal News,* whose editors, as has been said, saw that the reservoir would be a public improvement, and (at least so far as the companies could see from their side, which perhaps was not the best vantage point) without initial support from any responsible organization, a group of local people stirred up large numbers of the good folk of Rockland County to believe that their welfare was imperilled

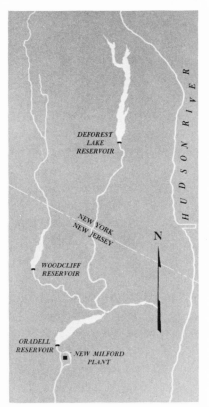

Reservoirs After Completion of DeForest Lake

beyond conception by a four and a half mile long lake on the site of a swamp that was threatened with ill-conceived housing developments. It would require years of study to determine what started the waves of panic that swept through the County, whether the instigators had some special talent for touching deep wells of human emotions and fears, or whether there was some special reason why the emotions of people of the area were unstable at that precise time, so unstable that a very slight push would topple them, or whether, on the other hand, there is always just below the surface a deep distrust of public utilities —painful as it is to contemplate, possibly only of water utilities— that needs but a small incident to set off a panic. The history of the reservoir would be a most useful topic for study in depth by those who are interested in group psychology. With due allowances for Water Company bias, it is hard to believe that another case history could be found of so meritorious a project which produced so great a mass hysteria.

So far as the water companies could see, the people whose homes were to be taken by the project were not the leaders in the opposition. There were one or two who were going to lose swampland a quarter-mile or so from their homes who persuaded themselves that a lake would injure them in some way, but most of the opponents appeared to be well-meaning civic-minded people with no personal stake in the situation, people of the sort who seem always to be active in such causes. They were soon joined by numbers of other local people with some claim to status as community leaders.

There were possible contributing factors, none of them very impressive. The plan to build the Tappan Zee Bridge and the New York Thruway threatened Rockland County's isolation, and some of its residents may have been uneasy on that score. Exactly the opposite has been suggested, that the Bear Mountain Park had withdrawn a large part of the County from development, and the public authorities were (mistakenly) concerned that the reservoir would mean another loss of ratables. To some of the good people of Rockland County, who chose to forget that the waters of the Hackensack had flowed into New Jersey since the time of the last glacier, and would continue to flow with or without a reservoir, the fact that people in New Jersey were to benefit from the water storage was objection enough; the reservoir was a scheme of New Jersey people to steal Rockland County's water.

One factor in the situation may have been that the County

was in many ways an "exurbanite" area, with more than its share of people employed in the so-called "arts" and communications, many of whom looked on the whole workaday world with suspicion and, whatever their credentials for judgment, had great talent for influencing others. Some few were well known figures in the theatrical world, ever ready to lend their names to any worthy and well publicized project. It would be wrong, however, to suggest that the hysteria did not affect other people as well. With the opinion-makers to point the way, volunteer firemen, Chamber of Commerce members and all manner of ordinary people stepped forward to join the crusade.

An easy explanation would be that it was simply one more case of a failure of a utility company to use modern public relations methods. One can be fairly sophisticated and still question that view. The Spring Valley Water Company, then and now, seems to enjoy good relations with the public, and it made great efforts to keep the public informed. Though misstatements of fact were freely used against the reservoir, there was little evidence that the basic opposition was based on a misunderstanding of the facts. People knew the essential facts about the reservoir very well. The local paper stood aloof from the controversy and carried a good deal of factual material on the subject. The case seems to have involved more than a failure of public relations; one would have to be a cynic indeed to believe that a shrewd public relations expert could have changed the vituperation and hatred that marked the opposition to the reservoir into a reasonable consideration of the facts.

An "Anti-Reservoir Association" was formed. Social functions were held to raise money to hire counsel and to publish newspaper advertisements exposing the evils of a reservoir. No stone was left unturned. Celebrities of the world of show business, radio, television and the arts were enlisted to dramatize the threat to the County. The County Board of Supervisors passed a formal resolution in opposition. Few, if any, important business people were involved, and, of course, no one knew what the ordinary commuter and the ordinary working man thought of the furore, but for others it was a gala time, long to be remembered in Rockland County.

The Anti-Reservoir Association mounted a very professional campaign. One cartoon, which showed an old reprobate, labelled Spring Valley, surreptiously handing over jugs labelled "$$$$$" to an even worse looking character who was putting it in a truck "for our dear neighbors in New Jersey," was of far better quality than the average editorial cartoon in a small daily paper, and the accompanying copy had an equally professional touch: "This Petition is a Barefaced Land Grab!" it warned, and went on to suggest that the whole project was merely a cover for a plan to take over 1700 acres of Rockland's valuable land. The logic was not impeccable. Why anyone would want to grab the particular swamp for something other than a reservoir, and to pay exorbitant prices for it, was not made clear; indeed, the writer had so little confidence in his point that no reservoir was to be built that he added a further observation that when it was completed the reservoir would bring miles of "smelly mud flats" to Clarkstown. Nevertheless, the end result was most persuasive, well calculated to convince the casual reader that the Anti-Reservoir Association had uncovered a barefaced plot to steal, or at least to despoil, a large tract of Rockland County land. The cartoon was only one of a barrage of publicity releases which left the general impression that a reservoir in which New Jersey would share the benefits was a slightly more offensive use of the swamp than an automobile junkyard, from which, at least, New Jersey would draw no benefit. So successful was the campaign that once it was well under way, no one in the County dared to raise his voice in public opposition.

One particularly difficult situation arose, which brought furrows to the brows of those whose memories went back to the time that the 75 foot elevation Rivervale reservoir site had been

Anti-Reservoir Campaign Cartoon, 1951

destroyed by the Rockland State Hospital. It was announced that a high school was to be built on the west side of the reservoir, with its athletic fields on the low land within the flood lines. It took little imagination to see that the school site could be a real threat if the loud-spoken Anti-Reservoir Association could dictate policy to the school board. Fortunately for both the school children of Clarkstown and the people of the Hackensack Valley, conferences with the board soon made it clear that it was interested in the best possible site for a school, not in public controversy, and an arrangement was worked out under which the Spring Valley Company acquired a far more attractive tract of land on high ground for the school, and exchanged it for the low-lying tract which might have blocked the reservoir.

In due time the Water Policy and Control Commission scheduled hearings at New City, with Mr. John C. Thompson, its Executive Engineer, in charge. Knowing the strength of the opposition, Spring Valley's case was advanced with care and in detail by Randall J. LeBoeuf, Esq., a leading water rights expert retained as counsel for the purpose. The Company showed precisely what land was to be flooded and what would be required for protective purposes around the reservoir, it outlined the financing plans, it showed that the growth of Rockland

County would require water from the reservoir within a relatively few years, it showed its plans for a filtration plant and pumping station to utilize the water, it showed that present river flows were very low in periods of drought—producing a "safe yield" of no more than a million gallons or so a day—and that the proposed reservoir, by utilizing floodwaters, could produce a "safe yield" of about 20,000,000 gallons a day.

The Anti-Reservoir Association then brought up its own guns. Without funds to produce capable witnesses, if indeed any capable witness could have been hired to support its case, and with clients seemingly more interested in abusing the Water Companies than helping their cause, counsel for the Association faced an unenviable task. Witnesses were produced to assert that the whole plan was a scheme to benefit the people of New Jersey, since the population served by the Spring Valley Company would never reach the numbers estimated by the Company. (The estimates have since proved remarkably accurate, if somewhat too conservative.) That local people should be asked to suffer a lake in their midst to benefit outsiders was, of course, unthinkable. One water expert was on the stand for days explaining that Rockland County was, in effect, floating on an inexhaustible reservoir of readily available ground water, which made it ridiculous to consider a surface supply. The same witness solemnly averred that raising the water level of the swamp would in some miraculous fashion lower the level of nearby ground water and ruin neighbors' wells.

The merchants of one small town, not then or since regarded as a shopping center, testified that the lake would destroy their town as a hub of commerce by making it impossible to build the network of highways which they envisioned as feeding a stream of traffic to their doors. Volunteer firemen were produced to assure the examiner that the reservoir would interfere with their good works, contrary to the common view that an abundant supply of water is helpful to firefighters.

Ladies from the Audubon Society trembled for the birds displaced by the water, and a local association of hunters testified that a lake would interfere with their plans to shoot the same birds. (When the reservoir was completed, the New York papers carried lengthy stories about the egrets that were attracted to the County for the first time by the new lake). A witness for the local conservation society took the stand to express its concern, the society presumably having no faith in reservoirs as instruments of water conservation. A respected physician of the neighborhood was reported to hold the professional opinion that a reservoir would bring on an epidemic of malaria, from which the area had anciently suffered. Acting on the principle of the Spanish proverb that any stick is good enough to throw at a dog, no one in the County who could imagine some reason why a reservoir threatened his peace and security was denied his place on the witness stand, and no witness for the Anti-Reservoir Association, however farfetched his story, failed to evoke a hearty response from its followers in the court room, who often acted as if they were attending a sporting match rather than a judicial proceeding.

In due time the hearings ended and the Water Policy and Control Commission entered an order approving the plans for the reservoir. An appeal to the courts by the Anti-Reservoir Association having proved fruitless, construction went forward rapidly, and on March 13, 1957, the project was formally dedicated. It was named DeForest Lake, in memory of Mr. Henry L. deForest, under whose Presidency the lake had been conceived. Mr. deForest had died about a year earlier. By the time the reservoir was filled, most of the people of Rockland County probably shared the views of the *Journal News* about it:

> "Guess it wouldn't be amiss to take a look at the lake that's stretching up from West Nyack in what used to be the Hackensack swamp.

Aerial View of DeForest Lake, 1968
Fred Van Dyke

"Well, the job is complete so far as the heavy clearing, ex-
cavating, grading and water impounding go. The water
has backed up well beyond the old Congers-New City
Road and well over the bridge that crossed the Hackensack
Creek. Down at the south end a few miles there's the dam

over which water has spilled and inching slowly up the shore line toward the intended level are several billion gallons of water. If there hadn't been the clearing and the dam, most of those gallons would now be out in the salty ocean without having done any good for anyone.

"There's one thing you can't figure in dollars and cents although you can say with fair certainty that a million dollars in scenic value has been added to the country by creation of the new reservoir. When you drive close along either shore or look north from the dam or north and south from the road crossing, you're looking at a beautiful body of water, a green shore line where there used to be only green trees you couldn't see through too well unless you were up high enough. It may be that as the season wears on, as well as others to follow, that prolonged dry weather will pull down the water level, leave more of the shoreline exposed. That we'll have to wait to see but currently there's benefit and the drawback yet to be determined.

"Financially, the picture is on the benefit side. All through the reservoir hassle we heard about this water being impounded for the people of another state, Rockland County interests left as cold as the brine pipes in a refrigerating plant. . . . We can't help but feel the county is giving away not as much water as it used to give, getting for it an entirely new source of tax revenue.

"As to drawbacks, we've lost some things we used to enjoy. There isn't any more swimming at the bridge by Sweet Clover Farm, at the clayhole further down, at other odd spots up and down the stream where the water was deep enough. We aren't going to get any bathing beach in return since the water is impounded for human consumption. We have lost some miles of trout stream, pretty well whipped every year and of no value if it hadn't been stocked by the Conservation Department. We've lost some thousands of snapping turtles by accident but that's an unmitigated blessing. We've lost some cover for game and the lake probably decimated the thousands of water snakes that used to abound. We've lost a refuge for one kind of birds but gained a refuge for other varieties.

". . . We've lost some houses and some others have had to be moved. The property has been paid for and arguments are continuing in some cases as to actual values but it has all been a matter of negotiation or commission settlement. We've heard 'confiscation' claimed but we can't agree because valuations have been determined at the going rate for real estate in the area. Maybe we'll have less flooding south of the dam. . . .

"Balance them all up and we really think the town and county are ahead of the game rather than losing everything, and gaining nothing. Moreover, we think the water company will be a good neighbor for it would be poor policy to be otherwise." (*The Journal News, June 18, 1956.*)

Twelve years later it is hard to believe that there is a single person in the County who would willingly see DeForest Lake drained and its land filled with development houses.

*   *   *

The day-to-day work of furnishing water to almost a million people and of planning how to continue to provide water for the ever-increasing population of northeastern New Jersey and Rockland County, New York, is of course, much more a part of the history of the Hackensack Water Company than its controversies. At the end of 1950, the year in which George H. Buck became President, the two companies served 105,000 customers (a population of about 500,000), had about $40,000,000 of plant and equipment, owned about 1,200 miles of mains, and on the average pumped out about 47,000,000 gallons a day. At the end of 1968, the number of customers had increased 81% to about 190,000, the amount of plant and equipment had increased 225% to almost $130,000,000, the number of miles of mains had increased 100% to about 2,400, and the average pumpage to the distribution system had increased 110% to about 99,000,000 gallons a day.

When Mr. Buck became President he found that Charles Alfke had gathered together over the last twenty years, with Mr. deForest's cooperation, an able and dedicated operating staff that made it unnecessary to follow Mr. Hill's example and bring in numbers of new people to deal with the problems created by the new suburban population explosion. Besides Mr. Alfke himself, who continued his important duties as Executive Vice President, there were (to name only those whose names appeared in the table of Executive Staff in the next Annual Report) Emile J. Fricker, Vice President, John C. Schlicht, Treasurer and General Superintendent of Construction Service, George F. Wieghardt, Chief Engineer, Walter H. Boquist, Comptroller, Julius Von Scheidt (now Vice President) Assistant to Vice President, Assistant Secretary and Personnel Director, Samuel W. Zerman (now Vice President) Attorney, M. Warren Cowles, Health Officer, Adolph Damiano, Assistant (and later) Chief Engineer, Harrison R. Cady, Mechanical Engineer, George F. MacCoubrey, Superintendent of Pumping Stations, Peter E. Pallo, Sanitary Engineer, Anthony F. Coviello, Assistant Comptroller, Josephus W. Hughes, Commercial Agent, Anthony Zoeller, Superintendent of Meters, John W. Lipinski, Assistant Secretary, Victor P. Aldoretta, Assistant Treasurer, and Wesley W. Gutteridge, Superintendent of the Spring Valley Water Company. Most of them were backed by a thoroughly capable technical staff.

In 1954, six new filter units were added to the New Milford Purification Plant, increasing the effective capacity about 45%.

Aerial View of New Milford Plant, 1968
Fred Van Dyke

Additional pumps were installed in the New Milford station, which was also largely converted to electric power. A number of elevated and ground storage tanks were built throughout the system to increase reliability and to maintain pressures. The New Durham Pumping Station was converted from a steam to an electric pumping station. Huge transmission lines were laid to reinforce the system as demands increased.

In 1958, the Borough of Montvale, in northeastern Bergen County, voted in a municipal referendum to sell the borough's water system to the Company, a particularly flattering development in view of trends to public ownership in other parts of the country. Not everything that happened in that year was as pleasing. The Company had been obliged to ask for rate increases to cover the cost of its huge property additions, not the least of which was the $8,000,000 DeForest Lake Reservoir, and in protracted hearings Samuel W. Zerman, the Company's Attorney, had submitted what the Company considered a compelling set of facts to justify the increase. The consumers principally affected were large industrial users, which, a study showed, were not bearing their share of the increased costs. With no knowledge of the complicated inter-company arrangements that had been necessary to build DeForest Lake, these customers evidently assumed, or affected to assume, that the complications were mere devices to hide a scheme to mulct the public. They therefore focussed their attack on the inter-company contract, and were so persuasive that they induced the dominant members of the New Jersey Commission (who no longer serve in that capacity), in an otherwise unexceptionable decision, to rule that the Hackensack Water Company ought to bear, not what the contract provided (95% of the charges) but only about one-half of that amount, and that Spring Valley, which was not using the reservoir at all and, indeed, had no facilities to use it, was to pay half the cost. Though the Company probably failed to see that from the Commission's standpoint, the reservoir had just been placed in service and experience had not yet proved its tangible benefits, the ruling seemed to it at the time not only to flout common sense, but to be wholly inconsistent with the financing plan which the Commission itself had carefully reviewed before the reservoir was built. The Commission then compounded the problem by an erroneous determination of the effect of income taxes on the transaction. The Company, which should perhaps have been more philosophical about the matter, was extremely distressed. A substantial amount of money was involved, for the net effect of the two errors was a ruling that Hackensack Water Company customers were obliged to bear only a little more than one-quarter of the cost of a reservoir of which they were the sole current beneficiaries. Even more important was the principle. Many had predicted that an interstate reservoir would give each state an opportunity to repudiate its share of the costs, and their worst fears seemed to have been realized. An appeal to the courts remedied only a part of the error. It was a worrisome situation while it lasted, but the next time the matter came before the Commission the Company was able to show by several years of actual experience how critical was the importance of DeForest Lake to the Company's consumers, and the Commission readily agreed that allocations of cost should be based substantially on the intercompany contract. The ancient Dutch proverb that trees do not grow to the skies is a great comfort in the water business.

*   *   *

By 1950 and 1960, it had become clear that a major addition to the Company's pumping and filtration was required, and that the New Milford Plant, located as it was on an island in the river, could not be sufficiently enlarged to meet the needs of the system. Plans were accordingly made for a new 50,000,000 gallon a day filtration plant (with an initial installation of units for half that capacity) on a forty-acre tract in Haworth, on the eastern shore of Oradell Reservoir about a mile north of the old plant. The new Haworth Plant was put into service in the summer of 1964.

At the same time, as the Company had foreseen, demands on the Spring Valley system during peak loads began to outrun the capacity of Spring Valley's well supplies, and a 5,000,000 gallon a day pumping station and filter plant was designed and built at the dam at the southern end of DeForest Lake. (It has since been enlarged to a capacity for maximum peak loads of 10,000,000 gallons a day.)

In 1964 the Company bought the small water system of the Bogota Water Company, which served about 1,200 customers in an area wholly surrounded by Hackensack Water Company territory. Shortly thereafter, following a public referendum, the Company also bought the municipal water system of the Borough of Franklin Lakes, a rapidly growing community in the western part of Bergen County separated by about five miles from the existing distribution system. On October 29, 1965, the Spring Valley Company bought the water system of the Haverstraw Division of Utilities & Industries Corp., which served about 5,300 customers in the Villages of Haverstraw and West Haverstraw and the towns of Haverstraw and Stony Point. As

Aerial View of Haworth Plant, 1968
Fred Van Dyke

a result of the latter purchase, the Hackensack and Spring Valley Companies serve the western shore of the Hudson River from the Lincoln Tunnel to the Bear Mountain Park. Negotiations for the acquisition of the Montvale system were handled principally by Mr. Fricker and Mr. Julius Von Scheidt. Having worked closely with Mr. Fricker and taken over his work upon his retirement, Mr. Von Scheidt was responsible for the later acquisitions. Mr. Von Scheidt, who was born on one of the last farms within the boundaries of the City of New York (where LaGuardia Airport now stands), has had a career that has borne an amazing resemblance to Mr. Fricker's. They both began work with the Company as secretaries at the age of sixteen—Mr. Fricker to Mr. French; Mr. Von Scheidt to Mr. Fricker—they both first became an Assistant to the President and later a Vice President of the Company. The Company takes great pride in the large number of its officers and employees who have devoted their entire business lives to the service of the people of Hudson, Bergen and Rockland Counties. Mr. Fricker and Mr. Von Scheidt are only two of many examples.

The early years of the 1960's were perhaps most notable in the history of the Company, not for acquisitions or capital expenditures, but for the unprecedented drought that struck the whole northeastern part of the United States during those years. Except for the years 1958 and 1960, which had rainfalls slightly above average, rainfall for the entire eleven years from 1955 through 1965 was below normal, and in the years 1963, 1964 and 1965 it was so far below normal as to threaten the area with disaster. Rainfall at New Milford for 1965 was only 26.01 inches, as compared with a normal rainfall of 42.70 inches. No drought in recorded history had lasted so long. It was far more severe than the 1932 drought and the long dry spell between 1904 and 1917, and with the great increase in population in the northeastern states, even a lesser drought would have been a very serious matter indeed. On June 12, 1965, Governor Richard J. Hughes declared a state of emergency imposing restrictions on the use of water in the four northern counties of the State, and in August President Lyndon B. Johnson declared Morris, Sussex and Warren Counties, along with many others in New York and Pennsylvania, to be Federal Disaster Areas. Many reservoirs were down to fifty percent of capacity.

It is a worrisome thing to be responsible for the water supply of hundreds of thousands of people when no water falls from the skies. Some of the older men in the Company had once been amused by Henry deForest's stories about making daily visits to the Weather Bureau during the 1932 drought, as if he be-

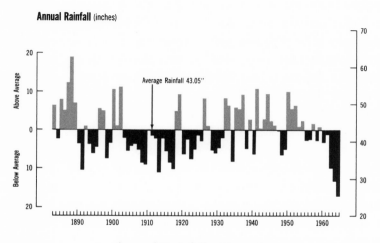

Annual Rainfall 1885-1965.
Courtesy New York Times

lieved that he was helping the situation by his concern. If they knew of any more productive measures to produce rainfall in 1965 than visiting the Weather Bureau, they kept them to themselves. Even the decision to put restrictions against the use of water into effect is a difficult one, for large numbers of people are dependent on free and full use of water.

Spring Valley customers, backed by DeForest Lake, went through the drought under no restrictions whatever, and Hackensack customers, thanks to their own conservation of water and the Company's long-term planning and huge capital expenditures for reservoirs, were restricted less by reason of local needs than in the fear that Hackensack water would have to be diverted to areas like Newark, which had done little or nothing either in the way of planning or conservation. The Hackensack Water Company and the Spring Valley Water Company had spent more than $16,000,000 in the ten years before the drought in providing new supplies and protecting old supplies against the day when no rain fell. Water Company people could perhaps be excused if, in the midst of their worries, they sometimes reflected uncharitably on the people who had tried so hard to prevent the construction of DeForest Lake a few years before, a lake whose waters now stood between the people of Rockland and Bergen Counties and disaster. They need have had no concern, for there was every reason to believe that with all of the current excitement about water shortages, the same people who had then been attacking the reservoir were now great supporters of water conservation, demanding that public officials show more foresight in protecting water supplies. There was also every reason to suppose that their zeal for water conservation would last until the next well-publicized cause attracted their fancy.

*   *   *

The decision to add an additional reservoir on the Rivervale site chosen by Nicholas S. Hill, Jr., forty years earlier, would not have been hard even without the drought. In the middle of a drought, even the most captious person could hardly say that the construction of an additional reservoir was unnecessary; indeed, one would have had to wait only a year or so to prove its necessity, drought or no drought. Perhaps because the need was so obvious, or perhaps because local people had the sense to see that a reservoir was infinitely more desirable for their

Lake Tappan Dam, completed 1967
Fred Van Dyke

community than any likely alternative, New Jersey Reservoir No. 3, as it was known in the planning stage, raised no storm of local protest. The Company was delayed somewhat by bureaucratic difficulties and by dilatory litigation by some of the towns, litigation which seemed monstrous in the middle of a drought when every drop of water was irreplaceable, but as it turned out the delay was not very serious.

The reservoir was named Lake Tappan, after the Indian tribe who were the original inhabitants of that part of the Hackensack Valley. With a dam at elevation 55, Lake Tappan adds 43% to the storage capacity on the river. It covers 1255 acres in Rivervale and Old Tappan, in New Jersey, and in Clarkstown, New York and, sad to say, completes the full development of the Hackensack River as a public water supply. The principal speaker at the dedication was Robert A. Roe, Commissioner of the Department of Conservation and Economic Development for the State of New Jersey, a man who had worked tirelessly during the drought to minimize its effect on New Jersey and knew from painful experience the supreme importance of water conservation. He pointed out that the lake was "a perfect example of how private enterprise gets things done." It had taken the Hackensack Water Company about two years to build it, compared with the seven that the state of New Jersey had needed to build the Round Valley Reservoir. Lake Tappan was also an excellent example of the ability of private enterprise to carry out long-term planning, for the Company had been acquiring land in the area over a period of forty years. It would have been impossible for any lake at all to be built if Nicholas S. Hill, Jr., had not had the foresight to preempt the land for water supply use before it was lost to real estate developers.

*   *   *

To anyone who has known the hundreds of people who have dedicated their lives to the Hackensack Water Company and the Spring Valley Water Company, a history such as this is in a sense no history at all, for the Water Company is the people who have carried on its work over the hundred years, quietly and without fanfare, from the man trudging behind a wheelbarrow at the Cherry Hill Pumping Station in the 1880's to the most sophisticated engineer planning new filter plants in the 1960's. Multitudes of people, living and dead, press themselves on anyone whose task it is to record the events of the last hundred years, particularly if, like the writer, he has known and admired the men and women who make up the Hackensack Water Company for more than a third of that century. But in another sense it is a very proper history, for the Company's pumping stations and the network of pipes that carry water out to hundreds of thousands of people, and the people who man them, are much like the heart and bloodstream of a living body, which work day and night carrying a burden as great and as vital as any other part of the body, a burden of which all of us are wholly oblivious most of the time. Like the heart and bloodstream, a water system serves its function best when it is least thought of; perhaps that is why water people prefer quiet respect to public notice.

Index

French, D. W., 91, 109-113, 134-140, 148, 161, 167, 168, 171, 172, 188, 219
Fricker, Emile J., 139, 140, 152, 171, 172, 192, 214, 219
Fuller, George W., 96, 104, 110, 111, 176
Fuller, George W. Memorial Award, 176
Furby, Mr. and Mrs. W., 9

Gamewell, 11, 48
Garfield, 93
George Washington Bridge, 172, 181, 186
Goetschius, John Henry, 14
Goslee, Robert W., 18
Gould, Jay, 27, 29, 40
Grandview, 141
Grant, Mayor, 128
Grant, General U. S., 15, 18, 28, 29, 40, 89, 161
Grant, Major U. S., III, 161
Greeley, Horace, 40
Griffith, D. W., 160
Gutteridge, Wesley W., 192, 214

Haas, Nelson, 48
Hackensack, 2-27, 30, 31, 33-36, 38, 39, 41-43, 45-49, 56, 61, 75, 93, 104, 145, 180N
Hackensack Academy, 16, 27
Hackensack Board of Health, 111, 112, 146, 147, 148
Hackensack Creek, 8, 19, 211
Hackensack Extension Railroad, 11, 32
Hackensack Fire Department, 33N
Hackensack Gas Company, 8, 23
Hackensack Golf Club, 94
Hackensack Hospital, 128, 135
Hackensack House, 6, 46, 48
Hackensack Improvement Commission, 18, 30, 34, 46, 53
Hackensack and New York Railroad, 4, 5, 23
Hackensack Republican, 4, 26, 59, 74, 105, 121, 122, 123, 124, 125, 126, 127
Hackensack River, 26, 34, 49, 60, 61, 75, 76, 97, 114, 115, 150, 163, 167, 172, 196
Hackensack Trust Company, 94, 135
Hackensack Township, 50
Hackensack Water Company
    charter, 1869, 12; original system, 34; issues first stock, 35; bankruptcy, 53;

reorganized, 57; moves to New Milford, 67; serves Hoboken, 68; builds Weehawken Tower, 70; expands into new areas, 78; Englewood high pressure system, 84; filtration controversy, 95; begins Oradell Reservoir, 97; purchases Spring Valley system, 113; builds Woodcliff Reservoir, 115; builds filtration plant, 131; builds New Durham station, 135; enlarges filter plant, 143; alum scare, 146; expands, 151; enlarges Oradell Reservoir, 163; plans Rivervale Reservoir, 172; introduces activated-carbon treatment, 174; post-war expansion, 213; purchases Montvale system, 215; Haworth Plant, 217; purchases Bogota system, 217; purchases Franklin Lakes system, 218; constructs Lake Tappan, 221
Hague, Frank, 165, 166
Hardenburgh, Abram A., 53, 57
Harrington Park, 151, 163
Harrington Township, 20, 51
Hasbrouck Heights, 93
Haverstraw, 4, 218
Hawkey, Richard R., 24, 25, 26
Haworth, 128
Haworth Filtration Plant, 144, 217
Hayes, Rutherford B., 52
Hazen, Allen, 95, 96, 97, 103, 110, 111
Heath, M. W., 8
Hein, Henry, 192
Hennessey, Charles O'Connor, 154, 155
Hering and Fuller, 110
Hill, Nicholas S., 156, 157, 167, 168, 170-173, 187, 195, 196, 201, 221, 223
Hillsdale, 121, 128, 129, 151
Hillsdale Manor, 127, 129
Hobart, Garret A., 60
Hoboken, 49, 59-62, 68, 69, 74, 78, 89, 90, 92, 93, 136, 157, 163, 164, 165, 166
Hoboken Land and Improvement Company, 60
Hoboken Observer, 112
Hoboken Port of Embarkation, 161
Hoboken Water Commission, 60, 74, 76, 112
Hoboken & Weehawken Horse Car Company, 93
Hogan, Lawrence, 192
Holy Trinity Catholic Church, Hackensack, 3

230

White, Harold T., 135
White, Mayor, 159, 160
White, Pearl, 160
White Steamer, 139
Wieghardt, George, 170, 192, 195-199, 214
Wiley, Dr., 146, 147, 149
Wilson's Academy, 9, 27
Wilson, Woodrow, 152, 154, 155
Winthrop, John, 189
Winton Eben, 9, 24, 25, 30, 32, 36
Wise, Thomas, 159
Wood Ridge, 93
Woodcliff, 115, 116, 117, 120, 128
Woodcliff Lake, 130, 131, 202
Woodcliff Reservoir, 115, 119, 128, 129, 130, 135, 140

Works Progress Administration, 189
World War I, 161
World War II, 190
Wortendyke, 51
Wortendyke & Demarest, 10
Wortendyke's Hotel, 129
Wortendyke, Jacob R., 13

Yale University, 141

Zabriskie, Abraham O., 13, 22N, 32
Zabriskie's Hill, 42
Zabriskie, John C., 42, 43
Zabriskie, Peter, 6
Zerman, Samuel W., 180N, 192, 214, 216
Zingsem, G. N., 11, 12
Zoeller, Anthony, 214